XPEDITION

A SAILING AND CYCLING SHOCKER

BY

DANNY FITZ

Follow your heart, but watch your back!

CRUISING LIFE

Los Angeles • San Francisco

Cruising Life, Inc.
4727 Wilshire Blvd, Suite 601
Los Angeles, CA. 90010-3873

U.S. Library of Congress Registration Number: Txu-2-311-192
Hardcover: ISBN 979-8-9868542-0-5
Paperback: ISBN 979-8-9868542-1-2
eBook: ISBN 979-8-9868542-2-9
Audiobook: ISBN 979-8-9868542-3-6
Edited by Elizabeth Fuller
Cover Design by Cherie Fox
eBook Production by Digital Conversion Laboratories
Audiobook Sound Engineering by Foxtail Sound
Nor'Sea 27 layout courtesy of bluewaterboats.org

For more pictures and information, please visit:

Xpeditionbook.com

Dedicated to my son, Luke:

*My love for you is deeper than any ocean;
may you always follow your heart.*

*Special thanks to my wonderful wife, Darcy,
for supporting me in telling a story
from another time in my life
the way it needed to be told.*

With gratitude to Samantha and her family.

Based on a true story, from a few decades ago...

Names have been changed to avoid
getting sued (again) or worse...

Legal Disclaimer

s/v Marylee

 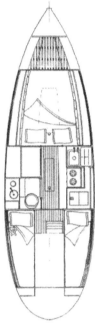

Make: Nor'Sea 27	Aux Power: 13 HP Diesel
Model: Aft Cockpit	Fuel Tankage: 27 gal.
Designer: Lyle Hess	Water Tankage: 40 gal.
Length: LWL 25'	Anchor: 35 lbs. CQR
Beam: 8'	Rode: 300' HT Chain
Draft: 3'10"	Electronics: GPS
Displacement: 8,100 lbs.	chartplotter, radar,
Ballast: 3,100 lbs.	autopilot, VHF radio, SSB
Sail Area: 394 sq. ft.	receiver, sat. phone, EPIRB.

Voyage of Marylee

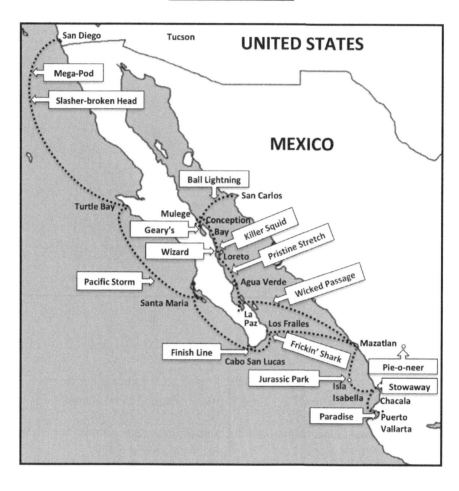

Route of Greeny

Table of Contents

Preamble
A Brave New World

By the dawn of the third millennium, cruisers, history's most decadent breed of explorer, plundered paradise purely for pleasure. With a fishing pole in one hand and a cocktail in the other – they quietly ruled the world.

Emboldened by technologies that would have astounded early explorers, they paraded around a predominantly peaceful planet. Up until recent times, the seas were uncharted, the natives were hostile, and owning a seaworthy vessel, let alone having the means to venture upon it, was unfathomable for the average man. That all changed. In the wake of globalization, cruisers took the helm.

Aboard fiberglass kingdoms of exquisite grace they crossed great oceans chasing the sun, to the distant anchorages of the brave new world where the fruits of paradise still hung. For at some point in history, impossible to pinpoint precisely when, the cannibals of yesteryear began accepting credit cards in lieu of eating men.

Chapter 1
Windows

Thar' be dragons out there –
lurking in the most unexpected places.

Have you ever wanted to get away? Away from it all? To live simply in nature – away from the things of man? Well, I sure did. For as long as I can remember I dreamt about sailing away to a palm-laden paradise with electric blue waters and white sand beaches.

That dream came true in the autumn of 2003, when I set out upon a sailing and cycling expedition that would become a cruiser legend. Of the numerous perils I'd face – the raging storms, lightning strikes, and reckless Italian drivers, I never envisioned being wanted by the cops, sideways with a murderer, sleeping with a loaded gun beside my bed, and defending myself in court. Nope, I didn't expect any of that. Settle in, my dear friends, for this tawdry tale of treachery should serve as a stern warning to any would-be wayfarers:

Follow your heart, but watch your back!

There are windows in life. Fleeting windows of opportunity to venture away from the snug harbor you've been sheltered in for way too long – to do something amazing. Something transformational. When one appeared in my thirties, I kicked that window wide open.

I longed to recapture the barefooted summers of my carefree youth when the warm August days went on forever. To sip the sweet nectar of freedom once again – not forever, but certainly longer than any company vacation policy would allow.

I was fortunate to have this opportunity. My blessings of good health, a supportive family, and a free and prosperous country cannot be denied. I own that privilege – yet make no apologies for it. For it was hard work, determination, and self-sacrifice that made this adventure possible. Those are the virtues I wish to impart. That is my intent. Work hard for your freedom – your life depends on it.

Looking back on all those rainy nights I slept in a tent on business trips, to get my industrial automation software company off the ground, only made its acquisition by a market leader that much sweeter. For everything truly fulfilling in life, everything that really matters, can only be achieved through self-sacrifice and hard work.

Naught without labor.

My perilous path to paradise would combine my two favorite sports – sailing and cycling. For boats and bikes, when properly paired, are the purest forms of propulsion. While they are both naturally powered and have unlimited range, they are opposite yet complementary, Yin and Yang, in terms of the places they go and benefits they provide. Spoiler alert: the beauty of sailing combined with the fitness of cycling is a fast track to self-actualization.

To me, sailboats are the physical embodiment of romance and freedom – the ultimate exploration vehicle. Like a spaceship, they're an autonomous microgrid of life-support systems that can take you places no other vehicle can. And once you arrive in paradise upon the wind, you can live there rent-free. Whether you're anchored off a secluded island in the South Pacific or a bustling harbor in the South of France, the moment you step back aboard, you are home.

The perception of cruising as being an elitist endeavor is wildly inaccurate. The vast majority of cruisers live frugally, going to great lengths to save money to keep their dream alive. Many will work odd jobs along the way – fixing diesel engines, cutting hair, or mending sails to stay afloat financially. Constantly enduring hardships, always rationing food, water, power, and fuel, they are some of the most down-to-earth people you'll ever meet. Most have become minimalists, having freed themselves from want, with limited space for possessions anyway. To them, the adventure is all that matters.

☼ ⚲ ☉

Even if you reach paradise in a canoe held together with duct tape, you're welcomed into a cruising community that will sacrifice themselves to help one another in the most extraordinary ways – like the group of men that sailed a thousand miles against treacherous winter seas to get a sick friend's boat home. It's a perfect society of self-sufficient souls that are coddled with camaraderie and common purpose.

Sailing has its seasons, though. Unless you're chasing an endless summer and crossing hemispheres, some are better than others. Since Mexico is hot in the summer with a constant threat of hurricanes, a decision was made to bikepack around Europe those months. That decision turned out to be a brilliant one.

Having already toured the U.S. west coast from Canada to Mexico, Montreal to Boston, and several countries in Europe, I knew a great secret. A great secret indeed. I knew that a tandem bicycle is one of the greatest inventions ever created and a godsend for like-minded couples. Working together as a team, sharing both elation and despair, the captain and stoker develop an inexplicable bond as they streak across the countryside. Tucked in tightly with minimal drag, the stoker is a second engine that makes the machine fly in the flats.

From the jungle coves of Mexico to the peaks of the Swiss Alps, it was poised to be the ultimate year off. We'd push away from the life we knew to venture out on the big broad blue. After all that preparation and planning, what could possibly go wrong?

Chapter 2
Decisions

On the steep rocky flanks where the redwoods reach the sea, Sam danced on the deck under a chandeliered night sky – too excited to stay in one place very long.

"I can't believe we're actually doing this; think we'll ever come back?"

"I hope not. Let's get south of the border and see."

"Margaritas anyone?" she said with a spin. "Once we're south of the border, we'll be free."

By every definition, Sam is a beautiful person – a petite blond with profound empathy who connects deeply with people within minutes of meeting them. We'd been dating for a little over a year before I brought up the idea of going cruising.

"Of course I'll sail off into the sunset with you. It sounds like a dream."

Compact and curious, with eagle-eye vision, she'd make a great first mate. The only downside was that she'd have to complete her graduate studies from afar – a small price to pay for some intrigue.

"If there's a will, there's a way, I just hope they don't take attendance."

School wouldn't be an obstacle for her. Sharp as a tack, she'd excel wherever she studied and would eventually earn a PhD. It was her grandparents' approval that weighed so heavily on her mind since they were helping finance her education. I overheard her on the phone with them:

"I wanted you to know about a trip Danny and I are planning."

. . .

"No, unfortunately, we're not coming to Indiana… We're sailing away on his sloop."

. . .

☼ ⚲ ◉

"Probably for a year; we're not exactly sure yet. We'll have to see how it goes."

...

"Yeah, he's taking a break from corporate life – sure can't blame him for that."

...

"It shouldn't be a problem. I can study anywhere and come home whenever I need to. Besides, I see this as an opportunity to enhance my education. Not only will I get better at languages, I'll learn a lot about geography, meteorology, marine biology, and other cultures too."

...

"Probably in late October. There's a cruising rally from San Diego to Cabo that's supposed to be a lot of fun. We'll probably do that. From there, we'll just go wherever the wind takes us, I guess."

...

"I know, and it's always been his dream."

...

"Really? Oh, that makes me feel so much better. I was hoping you'd say that."

...

"Don't worry, we will. Love you too. 'Bye."

Sam hung up the phone and started jumping for joy. "They're totally into it! They said they respected our decision and admired our courage."

"My dad said the same thing. As you get older, I believe you start seeing youth for what it really is – a form of wealth that's easy to squander, and impossible to recover. I mean, in the grand scheme of things, taking a year off only represents two percent of our working years, and going while we're relatively young and commitment-free seems like the right time to do it. Why not stop and smell the roses while they are most fragrant? If it means retiring a few years later, so be it; at least we'll have interesting stories to tell."

"Well, that's one way to look at it," Sam smirked. "Just know that some people will never understand why you'd quit your job to head out on some swashbuckling adventure. Even if they do go sailing, most people will wait until they're retired. To some, it may seem, well, kind of irresponsible."

"The irresponsible thing to do is spend forty-five years in a cubicle, putting cover sheets on TPS reports, without taking any real time for yourself. Life is fleeting, and it takes strength and stamina to survive out there. It's not easy carrying heavy provisions across a scorching hot marina or diving forty feet to free a fouled anchor. It's physically challenging, and there are times when there's no one around to help. In my opinion, the earlier you go, the more enjoyable it will be."

"You'll never regret this adventure, but you may miss what you're leaving behind."

She had a good point. It meant leaving the place I loved so dearly – after all that remodeling.

Perched on a bluff above the oceanfront enclave of Bello Beach, my home is my sanctuary. When I bought it, it was a trippy little hippie house with an ornate U-shaped bar that was built by the same guy that designed the interior of The Steve Miller Band's bus. Ironically, after what happened, it's situated just above a "clothing-optional" cove known as Little Beach. There was even a nakedness clause in the property disclosure that I signed, knowing full well that living above a nude beach would be both a blessing and a curse.

Aside from the stunning coastal views, the most unique thing about it is the brass fire pole I installed between floors – an underrated means of conveyance in my opinion. There's a reason why firehouses have 'em. With practice, you can slide down with a plate of food in one hand and a cocktail in the other – and climbing back up is always good exercise. I'll never forget my conversation with the pole salesman while shopping for it:

"I'd like to buy a brass pole."

"Alright, how long do you need it to be?"

"Around sixteen feet."

"And is this for dancing or sliding purposes?"

"Why does that matter?"

☼ 🏃 ◉

"Well, we recommend a two-inch diameter for dancing and a three-inch diameter for sliding. The increased surface area makes it easier to stop. So, is this for dancing or sliding?"

"Hopefully both. Does it come in two and a half?"

Chapter 3
The Right Boat

After graduating from college, I moved in with my monkey-blooded brother and best friend, Tim, in San Francisco. A charismatic extrovert and connoisseur of dive bars, he'll know everyone's name within five minutes of entering one – and be getting drinks bought for him within ten.

"Trust me, I'm a chemist," he likes to say as he hands you another libation. He spoke about writing a book about dive bars in Northern California using Neanderthal figures as a rating system. The more hunched-over and less evolved, the better.

Our apartment overlooking the bay was an excellent vantage point for viewing the nonstop parade of boats passing by. Seeing those colorful spinnakers racing across the bay every weekend inspired me to learn how to sail – so I started sneaking into private yacht clubs and loitering at the bar until I finagled my way aboard one.

My first outing was a complete disaster – when the boom the captain had me holding ripped from my hands, swung through the cockpit, and whacked him squarely across the head.

Thong!

He staggered to his feet and started screaming at me. Although it wasn't my fault, it should have been tied off with a jibe preventer. Let's just say it was an awkward trip back to the marina.

The second boat was a disaster, too. Before taking me out, they made me spend an entire weekend scraping, sanding, and painting the bottom all by myself. Then, when we did go out, we always crashed. We'd round-up, round-down, or just plain run into things – like docks and other boats. It all made sense after learning that this particular captain had nine DUIs and was no longer allowed to drive a car.

☼ ⚓ ◉

The third boat, however, was a charm. The crew was experienced and dedicated. We raced almost every weekend for several years and regularly won regattas – including a three-day race from Stockton around the south tower of the Golden Gate Bridge and back to Stockton. There were some tense times in the narrow deep water channel when the enormous ships came bearing down on us. Since we'd be disqualified if we used the engine, we narrowly escaped on the wind.

At one point during the race, we decided to anchor in the Carquinez Strait rather than battle the incoming six-knot tide. We took great pleasure in watching the other boats drift backward as they tried to sail against it. It suddenly occurred to me that sailing is perhaps the only racing sport where you can take the lead by standing still.

Although it was a great way to learn how to sail, I grew tired of racing. A laid-back cruiser at heart, I longed for a slow boat to paradise. To do that, I needed my own boat.

Regardless of budget, finding the right boat is a daunting task. By the time I found Marylee, lovingly named after my mother, I'd stuck my nose in more bilges than I care to remember. For one reason or another, they were never right.

It's an emotional decision, especially for cruisers, because one's hopes, dreams, and survival rely on the fiberglass shell they select. Happiness and heartbreak are just a few laminates away – and paradise is thousands of miles. I wanted something small and simple, but most importantly, it had to be safe.

"Go small and go now," Kame Richards, a Bay Area sailmaker and racing legend, once advised me.

Size really does matter. Since marinas and boatyards charge fees based on boat length, small boats save a proverbial "boatload" of cash for the same amenities. The lower sailing forces also meant that Sam could operate Marylee by herself on night watches without needing to wake me up.

The first question most people ask when they hear you have a boat is, "How big is it?"

No one has ever been impressed when I respond, "27 feet." Rather, there's usually an awkward silence before they say, "Well, that's still pretty big," or something like that.

It is my belief that the optimum cruising boat is the smallest one you can tolerate living in. Don't get me wrong, I love big boats and appreciate the space, especially as I get older: it's just that the cost and complexity go up exponentially with each additional foot.

In terms of design, I sought a full keel. Generally speaking, the heavy ballast of a full-keel means greater stability in treacherous seas. Even if it capsizes, the boat will right itself – shrugging off tons of water as she rolls to the surface. And the smooth, continuous bottom protects the propeller – making it less likely to snag on fishing nets, kelp, and other hazards if you drive over them.

While many cruisers prefer a fin-keeled design because they are faster and easier to maneuver, the cut-away modified full-keel of the Nor'Sea 27 was fast enough and stout enough to be the best of both worlds.

When I saw Marylee, it was love at first sight. Her traditional lines are endearingly "shippy." She's considered a "double-ender" because she's pointy on both ends – a Viking proven design that's kind in following seas. With three thousand pounds of molten lead poured into a one-piece hull, this tiny "pocket cruiser" possesses the strength and stability of yachts twice her size. And because she floats in only four feet of water, we'd be able to anchor in the electric blue shallows nearest the beach – where the deep-draft vessels dare not go.

Her dainty size also meant marinas would always have room for her, and she'd be the darling of every anchorage. From my experience, the more endearing a vessel is, the more approachable it is.

The Nor'Sea 27 has another huge advantage – it's trailerable. She's a world cruiser that can be transported like a ski boat – with no wide-load restrictions on roadways. Not only did this mean I'd be able to drive her home from Mexico, rather than bashing her up the prevailing Pacific, it meant she could access lakes and other bodies of water other cruising boats can't reach.

☼   ⚓   ◉

It felt surreal when my offer was accepted. Although it was a pittance to pay in terms of yacht purchases, it was a giant leap forward in terms of realizing my dream. On my maiden voyage aboard Marylee, sailing her home for the first time with my buddy, Duck, it dawned on me that I'd become a captain of a capable boat with a bona fide license to go rogue. There's a strange comfort in owning an ejection pod, knowing you'll be drinking cocktails on the high seas if the cities ever burn.

Over the next year, Marylee was painstakingly refitted. I spent most evenings and weekends preparing her to face the sea. I gutted her mechanically and electrically and replaced every system myself so I'd know them intimately.

I cursed the confined space and toxic chemicals that required me to wear a respirator all day. By the time the work was completed, my hair was matted with epoxy, there were cuts all over my arms, and I felt as deranged as I looked. I'd lost weight, too, because, like a mad scientist locked in his laboratory, I'd forgotten to eat.

On her shakedown cruise out the Golden Gate, Marylee seemed as solid and seaworthy a vessel as any captain could ask for. My, what a difference a small fortune had made.

Chapter 4
Loose Ends

U nraveling life's entanglements is liberating – like scraping
barnacles from a hull. Each account and subscription I canceled
made me that much more nimble. The last call I made on my
mobile phone was to deactivate it. Then I tossed it in a trashcan… That felt
good.

Aside from a mortgage and a few months left on a car lease, I was
leaving debt and obligation free. There's no better feeling than that. In
order to afford the trip, though, I needed to rent my home – preferably
furnished to avoid the cost and hassle of putting my possessions in storage.
Unfortunately, home sales were brisk at the time, and I couldn't find a real
estate agency interested in handling rentals. Discouraged and with
mounting pressure from a looming departure date, I decided to post an
online ad. Within an hour, the phone rang:

"Hi, this is Gamora, Violet Storm's personal assistant calling about
the rental property in Bello Beach. Is it still available?"

"Yes, it's still available – I just posted the ad a few minutes ago.
Congratulations, you're caller number one."

"Oh, that's great. Violet is really excited about the location. Would
it be possible for her to see it tomorrow – say, around five?"

"Five works. We look forward to meeting her then."

As soon as I hung up, I started doing my happy dance. "Heck yeah,
heck yeah. Hey, Honey, there's a lady coming to see the house tomorrow.
Her "personal assistant" made an appointment for her."

"Personal assistant? I need a personal assistant."

How did I know Sam would say that?

The following day, a convertible sports car pulled up precisely at
five. A handsome young couple emerged and began walking up the garden
stairs to the front door. She was a striking brunette in a black slit-skirt

dress with high heels, and he had a sweater collegiately tied around his neck. Clean-cut and professional, they made a fetching first impression.

"Hi, I'm Violet, and this is my brother, Randy."

"Nice to meet you both, this is Sam, please come in."

"Oh, this is exactly what we're looking for," Violet said with such conviction that I knew we wouldn't be negotiating the rent. "I've always wanted to live at the beach. If I lived here, I'd never want to leave."

"Yeah, we love it here, but we're sailing away to Mexico, so we'll hopefully see a lot of beaches."

"Wow, that's exciting. How long do you plan to be gone?"

"We're not sure; we'll just have to see how it goes. That's why I'd like to start with a six-month lease and go month-to-month after that. Especially since I'll be out of the country, I need reliable and self-sufficient tenants."

"That's us. We both have jobs, receive monthly income from a trust fund, and my brother's nickname is "Handy Randy" because he's so good at fixing things."

After filling out the application, she handed me some additional paperwork.

"I assumed you'd want to check my credit report – so I brought you a copy. I'll be the only one signing the lease since Randy is already on one with his ex-girlfriend…long story."

As I was showing them around, Violet and I were briefly alone.

"I have a good feeling about you two."

"And I have a good feeling about you, too," she flirted.

I took them downstairs to show them the garage, and entered the key code to open the overhead garage door.

"Nice car!"

"Oh, thanks, it's leased. Let me know if you're interested in renting it, too – there are still a few months left on it."

"Unfortunately, I don't need a car, but some of my friends might. I'll ask around."

☼ 🕴 ⊙

As soon as they left, Sam started expressing her concerns: "I know you're anxious to get this place rented, but there's something about them that doesn't feel right."

"Seriously? What's not to like?"

"I don't know. Young trust funders with a beach house sounds like party central to me."

"I get that, but they have a steady income, are willing to pay the asking price, want it furnished, and can move in right away. It's only a six-month lease, so if it's not working out, I can terminate it then."

"You're probably right," she acquiesced. "If it means going sooner and staying longer, I'm all for it."

After verifying Violet's employment the next day, by a source I'd later question, I called her with the good news.

A few days later, she returned to sign the lease agreement with Gamora, her pretty blond personal assistant, with odd scratches across her face.

"Nice to meet you; I believe we spoke on the phone. Violet mentioned that you have a car that you're renting for a few months, too. I'm interested, may I please see it?"

"Sure, just follow me down to the garage."

"I'll take it," she said the moment she saw it. "Here's a copy of my credit report and driving record; let me know if you need anything else."

It seemed too good to be true – like the stars had magically aligned. So, after quickly glancing through the documents Gamora provided, I drafted a lease agreement for her to sign.

"I can't believe this is happening – now I have a nice car, just like all my friends. I feel like I should pay you for the first three months upfront."

Suppressing the red flag her comment raised, I responded, "No, that's okay, the first month's rent and security deposit are fine."

After I handed Violet the keys to my home and Gamora the keys to my car, Sam pulled an apple pie out of the oven that she'd made from scratch and presented it to them.

☼　ⵟ　☉

"You guys are so sweet," Violet charmed. "Have fun in Mexico and don't worry about a thing. Send lots of pictures."

It was obvious that Gamora hadn't driven a manual transmission before. The sound of grinding gears made me cringe – that car would never be the same. After a few stalled attempts, it finally lurched forward and sped off.

I was stoked. "The house and car are both rented; how lucky is that?"

Chapter 5
The Baja Ha-Ha

Every October, hordes of cruisers descend upon San Diego, readying their vessels to fly south for the winter in a cruising rally appropriately named the Baja Ha-Ha. The course skirts over 750-miles of desolate coastline, with nary a taco stand in between. It finishes at the tip of the Baja Peninsula and is informally consummated with an upside-down tequila shot in a smoky cantina in Cabo San Lucas. Historically speaking, the Ha-Ha is a sun-drenched glide to the tropics at that time of the year – the most favorable season to attempt it.

Over the years, the event has had a tremendous impact on West Coast cruising – launching thousands of swashbuckling adventures upon the open sea. There's an enduring comradely among boats flying the blue Ha-Ha burgees from their masts; most will fly it until it disintegrates in the tropical sun. Seeing one in a distant anchorage is like running into a friend in a faraway place.

The fat and tan majority will spend the winter lounging like lizards in the palm-laden coves of the Mexican Riviera. They'll dissipate come spring. Some will head north to the Sea of Cortez; others will head south to the Panama Canal and the Caribbean; and an intrepid few will cross the great ocean to the unrivaled South Pacific.

The class and caliber of boats vary greatly – from offshore veterans aboard twenty-ton passagemakers to scared shitless knuckleheads, like us, on the smallest boat in the fleet. The latter are too overwhelmed to think clearly and pray for fair weather because they've never sailed in anything but. It won't take long for their innocence to fade – as soon as the sea takes its first swipe at their lives.

In our case, it would only be a matter of days...

The rally consists of three legs with two stops along the way. The first leg, from San Diego to Turtle Bay, is the longest and usually takes three days. The second leg, from Turtle Bay to Bahia Santa Maria, traverses a treacherous coastline and usually takes two days. The final leg is shorter and warmer than the other two, as you wander into the tropics.

The two stops along the way provide the captains with an opportunity to socialize with people other than their insubordinate, cutthroat crew. Debauchery usually ensues – a naturally occurring byproduct when dreamers and outlaws mingle on the high seas. They become more hedonistic with each passing day. Rum-crazed bastards – every one of 'em. They've sold their homes, changed their names, and abandoned their kids in college.

It's a petri dish of piratical tendencies
where only the saltiest will survive.

The final hours before departure are complete chaos – as stressed-out cruisers run amuck through the streets, knees bent, in search of an elusive fix to a mission-critical system that just failed. There's less drama on Broadway. They talk too quickly, curse too often, and drink too heavily to make any sense. Best to give them a wide berth – for no good can come from associating with nervous newbies up against a deadline. Just know that beneath the matted hair, greasy shirts, and bloody forearms, they're good people just trying to make a starting line.

To our great fortune, "Slasher" signed on to be our middle-aged Canadian cabin boy. More crew meant more rest – and more rest meant more safety. Poor decisions at sea are usually bred from prolonged exhaustion. Despite his lack of sailing experience, his ability to stay awake for ridiculous lengths of time made him perfect for the role. A consummate engineer with logic too pure for average consumption, surely he would be an asset.

We nicknamed him "Slasher" after the slashing penalty in hockey, for his seductive slaying of seriously flawed women. A simple tomahawk chop between us would indicate his intent to slash or confirm a successful slashing. His nickname for me was "Danger Dan," but he usually just called me "Danger."

He arrived with a rigid suitcase that everyone, including him, loathed by the end of the trip. On a few occasions, his bulky luggage was almost tossed overboard.

In a salty tavern at the end of a wharf, we clinked schooners of beer, toasted death, and drowned our fears.

"Cheers, Rabbit Ears."

"How's the weather looking?" Slasher asked.

"Light air and flat seas for the first three days. We'll probably need to motor most of the way to Turtle Bay."

"Fine by me, I'd rather start in calm conditions than in a storm. It would be nice to catch some fish before I die."

"Not me," Sam said, "I'd rather have wind to sail by. It's so much more pleasant when that diesel isn't running."

Despite the fact that the crew knew Marylee well, we spent that evening practicing safety drills and abandon ship scenarios.

"As for the sleeping arrangements, Slasher, you'll be here," I said, pointing to a coffin-shaped quarterberth that required contortion to climb into.

"Dude, this totally sucks. You can't possibly expect someone of my size to sleep here."

"Well, not comfortably anyway. What did you expect in steerage class? Look, man, if you're not happy with your accommodations, feel free to sleep outside in the cockpit. There's definitely more room out there."

He took my advice to sleep under the stars and dream about America – the way all Canadians do. After we settled in for the night and everything became quiet, there was a strange sound emanating from the hull. I got up to investigate.

"Sammi, do you hear that?"

"I do, and it's weird; it's coming from all over."

Slasher poked his head inside and listened for a moment. "What the heck is that?"

Crack, crack, crack.

"I sure hope the hull wasn't structurally damaged when we trucked it down here. We can't go to sea in a compromised hull."

The morning light revealed another sobering revelation. The raging wildfires in the hills around San Diego had blanketed the city in an inch of black ash. Our boat and cabin boy were covered in it.

"Golly!" is much less profane than what I actually said when assessing the situation. "Slasher is going to have one hell of a time cleaning this up."

Hearing his name, he sat up in the cockpit. He didn't understand why we were laughing until he saw his sooty face in Sam's pocket mirror. After a group chuckle, I handed him a mop and went back to bed. It was impossible to sleep though – the bastard was scrubbing so loudly.

"Still," I thought to myself, "that's one hell of a cabin boy."

Once the topsides were tidied, we began searching for the source of the mysterious sound. Nothing was evident; there was no visible damage.

"The trip is on hold until we figure it out. It's not worth the risk."

"Maybe we should get a surveyor in to look at it?" Sam suggested.

"Good idea. I'm going to go talk to the riggers that tuned the mast; maybe they can help."

As I was walking up the dock, I overheard a conversation between two men on another boat that stopped me in my tracks.

"Boy, those crackling shrimp sure are loud in this marina. I had trouble falling asleep last night."

"Sorry to interrupt, but is that what that sound is? We were about to cancel our trip because we thought we had a cracked hull."

"You're not the first ones to think that. Last year, some Japanese sailors hauled their boat out and ground it down three times, looking for cracks, before someone finally told them about the shrimp. I'll bet those shrimp, coupled with a language barrier, cost them three months and thirty grand."

☸ ⚲ ⊙

Chapter 6
Shoving Off

To our chagrin, Grouchy, a wisecracking friend with endless one-liners, had ridden his motorcycle hundreds of miles through raging forest fires just to torment us before our departure. A master of annoyance, aggravation is his art.

"Yo Fitzy! Nice boat, Skippy; where's the rest of it?"

His ability to bother is legendary – systematically taunting friends or an innocent bystander who's in the wrong place at the wrong time. His intense wit and twisted rationale are distilled into Grouchyisms – life-coaching idioms such as:

"Don't get good at what you don't want to do – because everyone will always want you to do it."

He's the type of madman who eats dessert before his main course to make sure he saves room for it. He aspires to build a lair, affectionately known as "Camp Grouchy" – a quasi-military installation with perpetually idling tanks. Under Grouchian law, taxes, religion, holidays, and children are strictly forbidden. Left unattended and with enough money, he could become a supervillain of epic proportions – a true nemesis to the common man.

He sat in his zero-gravity chair all day, refusing to assist in any way, trying to convince Slasher to throw me overboard and sail away with Sam. Throughout my lame departure speech the next morning, he hummed the theme from Gilligan's Island and made "glug-glug" drowning noises.

Just before we pushed off, he presented Slasher with a stuffed animal, a pink elephant, declaring that it was his "spank-toy" for lonely late-night watches. Pinky, as it became known, was along for the ride – and Slasher seemed sheepishly content.

☸ 🕴 ☉

With Grouchy's vibrations too menacing to endure any longer, we had no choice but to depart. Suddenly, death at sea seemed less daunting. As we motored away from the dock, we could see him gesturing obscenities until he disappeared in the haze.

Well played, Mr. Grouchy... Well played indeed.

Chapter 7
Underway

Yanmar, our beloved thirteen-horsepower inboard diesel, purred like a pussycat as it pushed Marylee out of the estuary. The harbor seals sunning on the channel markers barked and waved their flippers as we rounded the mark.

"G'day, ladies."

Fetching a northerly breeze off Point Loma, the mainsail filled, and Marylee was gently lifted to sea. In the distance, there were silhouettes of sailboats maneuvering through the smoky air toward the ambiguous starting line. The blood-red sun on the glassy water gave the moment an apocalyptic feel. Ominous as it were, we unfurled the jib and joined the colorful fleet of spinnakers charging south. The event officially began when the Grand Poobah declared it so over the radio.

It was thrilling to be surrounded by so many boats sailing south to the little latitudes. At long last, Marylee was on the open ocean – where she belonged. Everything prior to that moment – the endless hours of work and pressure to make the deadline – suddenly became irrelevant. Reality was sinking in, though it felt like a dream. The ball of stress I'd carried around for months slid down my leg, rolled off my foot, and fell overboard with a splash.

Sam scanned the horizon with binoculars. "We should sleep well if these conditions hold; it's smooth as glass out here."

"It's a long way to Cabo," Slasher foreshadowed. "Let's just hope it stays that way."

The downside of sailing in a cruising rally is that the fleet departs based on a schedule rather than timing the weather windows and sea states. Sailing on a schedule can put fair-weather sailors, like us, in conditions they wouldn't normally go out in. The Ha-Ha event coordinators are extremely safety conscious and will postpone legs if it looks dangerous, but ultimately it's the captain's decision to go to sea and their responsibility to keep their crew safe.

⚓   ⚲   ◉

Before learning to sail, I always thought that a storm meant rain. At sea, I learned that it can consist solely of wind; that blue skies can be deadly; and that a landmass to hide behind can make a blustery day a whole lot better. A good captain is always aware of the closest shelter from the storm, even in the fairest of conditions.

In 2003, marine weather forecasting in Mexico was spotty at best. Like in the days before TV, gringo cruisers huddled around their SSB radios to hear forecasts from sailors-turned-meteorologists like "Don on Summer Passage, transmitting from Oxnard, California."

Mexico's long coastline, high mountains, and diverse climate make maritime weather complicated to predict. Understanding the bigger picture – of how landmasses, heat, tides, and winds affect sea states requires both local knowledge and practical experience. There are even times without wind when monstrous waves will march across oceans if opposing forces don't knock them down.

"These balmy conditions are nature's way of saying, "Cocktail, anyone?"

With that, Slasher jumped below to do what needed to be done. He emerged a few minutes later with a fresh pitcher of margaritas – and poured us each one.

"¿Por qué no?" I said as he handed me mine. The Spanish phrase for "why not?"

From that point on, "¿Por qué no?" became the obligatory response when offered an alcoholic beverage. At some point, we even began referring to beers as "Por qué no's."

Our conversations went like this:

"Por qué no?"

"¿Por qué no?"

Then you'd get handed a beer.

There's a widely held belief among captains that booze is the lubricant of a well-oiled crew. The correlation between alcohol and boating is one of nature's eternal mysteries... No clear separation between the two. For centuries, grog was the daily multivitamin the captain prescribed to ward off loneliness, anxiety, and dissention in the ranks. Accordingly, I

☼ ⚲ ⊙

insisted that my crew take steady doses of the juice to stave off mutiny. If they stayed tipsy enough, they'd pose no coordinated threat.

We overheard a radio conversation between a large catamaran and another boat. "Good wine is hard to find in Mexico; hopefully the eighteen cases we brought will last until we reach Panama."

And hey, hats off to the boat with the topless girls drinking from bottomless glasses… They're always welcome on the high seas. It's amazing how laid-back people get on a boat bound for paradise – a nautical phenomenon known as "porna-floatora."

One major difference between cruising and van life is that twenty-four miles offshore, you are in international waters. Out there, only maritime laws prevail. Although vessels are supposed to abide by the laws of the Flag State, the country in which the vessel is registered, one drawback of true freedom is that it manifests itself in a relatively lawless frontier where every crew member must be prepared to defend themselves.

We cheered the black triangle on the chartplotter, representing us, as it crossed into Mexican waters. Symbolically, we'd left the maritime safety net of the United States, but in actuality, we were already alone. Although we were traveling at the same speed as the rest of the fleet, by the time we reached the border, we couldn't see another boat in any direction. The immensity of the ocean is astounding, making any boat feel small.

Chapter 8
The Mega-Pod

Afteran uneventful night straddling the strand some forty miles offshore, visibility had noticeably improved by the next morning. Just as the smoke completely cleared, we came upon the most amazing display of nature any of us had ever seen – a mega-pod of dolphins feasting and frolicking as far as the eye could see. There were thousands of them. I pondered whether they'd congregated there just to get away from the smoke.

Taking great interest in our tiny sloop, they started jumping the bow as it cut through the water. They were flipping and spinning as if they were competing for our attention. Then, as if it had been choreographed by trainers, seven jumped in unison as Sam and I watched from the bow. Thankfully, Slasher captured the image that was chosen for the cover of this book. In all my years of sailing, I've never been so smitten with the sea.

The sunshine and dolphins brightened our mood. Under a powder blue sky on a cobalt sea, surely nothing could go wrong.

Then tragedy struck...

Without casting blame, it was entirely Slasher's fault.

"Um, guys, I've got some bad news," the culprit confessed, "I broke the toilet."

Becoming "headless" isn't immediately alarming. It takes several weeks of crapping into a clear plastic container placed at the bottom of the Slasher-broken head to fully appreciate a functioning one. In retrospect, parading the contents through the cockpit before emptying them overboard made the crew more intimate. Regretfully, though, for Slasher and me, it got competitive.

Standing dogwatch just after sundown on the third day, with the wind blowing sweetly through the well-trimmed sails, we ghosted between

Isla San Benitos and Isla Cedros – the largest offshore island on Baja's Pacific coast. The barks of elephant seals echoed off the rock walls of the San Benito rookery.

Marylee was several hundred miles south of San Diego now, as made apparent by the rise in air and sea temperatures. Outside, barefoot, with only a pair of board shorts on, I'd never felt happier. The warm breeze and flat seas created a soaring sensation at the helm – like Marylee was weightless on the water.

It's times like these that the beauty of sailing will leave you breathless – like the tingling sensation when you're falling in love. It is then that the purity of a wind-powered vessel will steal your heart, coming alive with moods and personalities. There are times when I'd swear Marylee was tired, and others when she seemed to gallop with glee.

The boat off our starboard beam, Luna Sea, hailed us on the radio. She'd come to an abrupt halt after snagging a fishing net – an ever-present hazard in these waters. Sometimes the only way to break free is to jump into the inky black ocean and cut away the ties that bind. Fortunately, they were able to clear the prop with a boat hook and begin moving again.

It was surprising to see so many open ponga boats fifty miles offshore in the middle of the night. The only lights they had were flashlights, which they shined at us as we approached. We weren't sure whether they were trying to warn us about nets in the water or just trying to be seen.

Otto, our faithful tiller-mounted autopilot, diligently held our course. Autopilots are fantastic inventions – a necessity for crews that have better things to do than steer. It's a mechanical solution to a monotonous problem; you just set a compass heading, and the machine tries to hold it.

Although autopilots make cruising much more enjoyable, it's easy to put too much trust in them. Of the half a dozen boats that sank while we were cruising in Mexico, a majority of them had left the autopilot unattended. Boats can be swept sideways as currents or conditions change, especially around capes, making the heading a moving target that needs constant adjustment.

☼ ⚓ ☉

With the exception of the Slasher-broken head, everything was working perfectly aboard Marylee. All those months of preparation were paying off. As the winds subsided, I fired up Yanmar and went below to get some rest. Surely nothing could go wrong now.

I was awakened by a commotion in the cockpit and noticed the absence of a familiar sound – the engine.

"I'm not sure what's going on," Slasher griped. "It started to sputter – then died. Could we be out of fuel?"

"Not likely, according to the fuel gauge, we still have half a tank."

We tried again and again to restart Yanmar. Knowing that a diesel engine only needs fuel, air, and compression to run, we suspected that there was air in the fuel line – but couldn't bleed it. I removed the inspection plate on the fuel tank and shined a flashlight into it.

"Yep, we're out of fuel. That sucks, I just replaced the gauge."

It was a learning experience. From that point on, I always carried spare fuel jugs and never trusted boat fuel gauges again. It wasn't very worrisome, though, because there was plenty of wind to sail by, and we were within thirty miles of our destination.

A primitive outpost in the middle of a lonely stretch of coastline, Turtle Bay is one of the most isolated villages in Baja. It's a blessing for mariners, though – one of the few natural harbors on Baja's Pacific coast. Between there and Ensenada, some 350-miles north, there isn't much shelter from the storm.

The sleepy little village swells in population two days a year – when the Ha-Ha comes to town. Restaurants that typically serve ten people a day are filled with hordes of red-faced gringos lying about this, that, and the other.

It's one of the dustiest places on earth, too; the locals wage a nonstop war with it. Undoubtedly, the happiest home in Turtle Bay is the one with the best broom. Occasionally a water truck will rumble by, spraying down the dirt roads, but that just creates mud so sticky it will suck your huaraches right off.

☼ 𐐚 ⊙

We took turns diving off the bow into the pea-green sea. It felt good to get some exercise, but the water was colder and cloudier than we expected so far south.

That evening, we dinghied to the Ha-Ha Halloween Party in our costumes. We must have looked like a clown car at a three-ring circus driving through the anchorage dressed as a butterfly, the Grim Reaper, and Dr. Evil.

The local children flocked around Sam, stroking her costume and following her around. It didn't take long for them to commandeer it. As a little boy flitted across the dance floor wearing her wings and antennas, his sister was reaping him around the neck with Slasher's Grim Reaper sickle.

Chapter 9
Clobbered

A fter weighing anchor the next morning, we toasted farewell to Turtle Bay – clinking coffee tumblers and praying for fair winds. "Hey Marylee, did you hear the weather forecast?" our friends on Soy Libre shouted as they pulled alongside us. "Bet you wish you had a bigger boat."

The forecast called for increasing winds and waves down the Baja Peninsula, so we anticipated some spirited sailing. We didn't, however, expect the freakish storm that dropped Halloween snow on the peaks around San Francisco to slide down the coast and clobber us.

Away from the snugness of Turtle Bay, roughly thirty miles offshore, ten-foot swells started marching in. Our double-ender rode up and down them with remarkable comfort as the seas built.

Slasher was impressed: "This is a great boat; she eats those waves up and spits them out."

"No doubt, she's at home out here. Otto, on the other hand, isn't faring as well."

As the forces on the rudder, known as "sea helm," build, the autopilot struggles to hold a course. As a result, we had to steer manually – something we took little pleasure in. Not only was it tedious, it meant the helmsman had to sit outside in the cockpit to get leverage on the tiller.

In normal conditions, we'd sit in the companionway during night watches. Situated just above the engine, it's a warm and safe spot where you can see all the instruments and operate the boat. We had a general rule that if you ever needed to go on deck at night, you must first wake up a crewmate to supervise. In these conditions, however, we had no choice but to sit outside, in the cold and lonely cockpit, and steer manually.

We kept a watchful eye out for rogue waves and other boats. In the deteriorating conditions, the radar was rendered useless because the large waves created so much surface scatter on the screen that they were impossible to discriminate from other vessels. So, as we crested each wave,

☼ 🚶 ◉

we looked around for running lights, hoping not to see a freighter bearing down on us through the frothy white madness. Several hours later, just after dawn, the sunlight confirmed what we already suspected.

"They're getting bigger. What do you say we go fishing to take our minds off it?"

"Good idea, Slash," I replied, knowing it wouldn't ease mine.

There wasn't any immediate cause for concern. Marylee was moving along nicely, and the seas were still manageable. Still, as the sun set, we all knew it was going to be a long night. Slasher and I were in the cockpit sipping Por qué no's when Sam opened the hatch to deliver some disturbing news.

"Guys, I was listening to the radio, and it does not sound good. People are saying that Punta Abreojos is really bad right now, and conditions are expected to get worse."

Slasher gauged it on the chartplotter: "We're about thirty miles from there right now – which means we'll be rounding it around midnight."

"Well, we can't turn back to Turtle Bay in these heavy seas even if we wanted to. Best to run with them or heave-to."

"What's heaving-to?" Slasher asked

"It's a survival technique where you stall the boat by back-winding the sails. As the boat drifts backward, it creates a slick that prevents the waves from breaking on it. It's a last resort, though; we'll get blown far out to sea. There isn't any protection inshore either – at least nothing I'm willing to attempt. The entire coastline is littered with rocks and shoals."

"We need to go further offshore," Sam said with certainty.

Slasher scoffed, "What? We're already thirty miles out… and you want to go further offshore?"

"I know it sounds counterintuitive, but we need to be in deeper water – away from the shallow bottom. Waves are pushed up as the seafloor shallows; I learned that in my sailing class. We need to be out here," she said, pointing to the darker blue region of the map.

"Sam's right, it gets a whole lot deeper just a few miles out."

☼ ⚹ ◉

Against our natural instinct of staying close to land, we changed our course to round the cape further offshore. The growling waves sounded like a freight train behind us.

"If she rolls, your safety harness will keep you attached to the boat. Hold on to something strong and protect your head."

Sam seemed concerned. "Do you really think we're going to capsize?"

"Not if it stays like this. Don't worry, we'll be alright, just hold on."

Our hope was that the wind and waves would diminish, as they often do, when thermally generated diurnal winds subside at night as the landmasses cool. This front, however, was bearing down from the Arctic Circle and had impressive scale and strength.

Late at night and all alone, Slasher piloted the boat through the enormous swells. It was remarkable how comfortable it was in my bunk. I slept soundly until it was time for my watch.

"How's it going out here?" I hollered over the screeching wind. "Any developments?"

"It's too dark to tell, but it seems pretty much the same. I'm so tired I can barely see straight."

"Grab some shuteye, buddy, and great work. Hopefully we're through the worst of it. By the time you wake up, we'll probably be anchored in Santa Maria cooking pancakes."

"That sure would be nice; I hope you're right."

He unhooked his harness and fell sloppily through the pitching companionway.

"Wake me if you need me," he said, collapsing on the berth where I'd just been sleeping – a common practice on submarines known as "hot bunking."

Alone in the cockpit on an inky black sea, I longed for daybreak. Unfortunately, the morning light only made the situation more frightening. As the wind increased, it shrieked through the rigging with a banshee cry. Disaster seemed imminent.

☼   ⚡   ◉

"Is this how it ends? Is this how I die?" I asked
myself, questioning my ability to manage the worsening
situation. "But she's a strong boat; she'll make it...."

The morbid flipside of being lost at sea is much less chronicled than survival. Dead men tell no tales. There's usually only speculation about what caused the doomed sailors to sadly watch the surface slip away. You never hear about the involuntary breath a drowning man takes before going into cardiac arrest. As his lungs fill, his vision fades – the burning taste of salt – then darkness.

As a precautionary measure, I woke up the crew and asked them to put on life jackets and get the ditch bag ready in case we needed to abandon ship. It contained food, water, flares, an emergency desalination watermaker, a first aid kit, and a handheld radio.

Sam hailed some nearby boats to exchange coordinates – so they'd know where to look if we were lost. We could hear several other vessels having difficulty – including a fifty-foot catamaran that had taken on several hundred gallons of seawater through an open transom hatch.

The sound of the whistling winds increased at the top of the waves and decreased as we fell into the troughs. At the bottom, we were surrounded by two massive walls of water.

"Oh my God, did you see that?" My voice trembled. "It's like being at the bottom of a ravine."

Slasher looked worried. "Oh man, they've got to be over twenty feet now."

"I've never seen anything like this; very few people will. Keep your eyes peeled for rogue waves because they can be twice the size of an average one."

It felt surreal, like a bad dream we couldn't wake from. Every fifteen seconds, Marylee was lifted high into the air as the waves marched under her keel. We'd accelerate down the faces, surfing, and sliding, only to lose momentum on the backside as the swells passed beneath us.

Although the theoretical maximum hull speed for a Nor'Sea 27 is around six knots, Marylee was careening down the faces at over eleven. At

✺   🜂   ◉

that speed, there's a propensity to nose-dive into a trough, submerge the bow, and cartwheel forward. This type of crash is known as "pitch-poling" and usually leads to a watery grave.

"Oh no!" Slasher shouted as he pointed to the mast. "The mainsail's coming apart!"

Indeed, the triple-reefed reduced sail had detached from the mast where two plastic slides had sheared.

"We've got to douse it!" I yelled. "We're way overpowered."

Dropping the mainsail in high seas is dangerous because someone must leave the safety of the cockpit to gather and tie it off. Between the enormous waves, slippery deck, and whipping canvas, it's easy to fall overboard.

"I'll get it, Danger. You steer."

Slasher clipped his harness onto the jackline, a safety line that runs along the deck, and crept forward.

"Be careful, Slasher," Sam pleaded. "Oh my gosh, Honey, please don't lose him."

I looked back at the large breakers coming for us and replied, "He'll be alright, but he needs to move quickly."

Standing at the mast, Slasher gathered and secured the sail as Sam eased the halyard, the rope that hoists the sails up the mast. Threat averted, he shuffled his way back to the cockpit. We grabbed him, pulled him to safety, and thanked him for a job well done.

Without a sail up, we now lacked stability. The boat rocked back and forth, making it harder to square up to the oncoming waves before they hit. I unfurled a tiny amount of jib, about the sail area of a T-shirt, and secured it. The tiny canvas had a huge effect on steerage, making the ride more balanced and controllable.

Looking out on the madness, I reflected on the investments I'd made in safety equipment. I knew it would be difficult to deploy a life raft in these heavy seas – and even if we were able to, there wasn't a boat in the fleet that could pluck us from it. We accepted the fact that we were sailing for our lives. We had to make Santa Maria. We just had to.

⚓ ⛵ ◉

Piloting a small boat through large waves leaves little room for error. Marylee was pushed sideways again and again as the waves slapped her transom. Even with good leverage on the tiller, it took strength to maneuver her.

Several grueling hours went by. The biggest downside of an ocean storm is that the terror can last for days – wearing you down until you finally make a mistake.

We sealed the companionway with clear Plexiglas drop boards so the water couldn't rush in and flood the cabin. The normally watertight port windows were leaking, though – a leak you'll only discover when they are completely submerged. They looked like front-load washing machines with foamy water sloshing around.

"Sorry to get you guys into this; this was supposed to be fun. If it gets too rough, we'll just go below and hold on for dear life. Marylee will take care of us."

"Just keep doing what you're doing, guys!" Sam cheered. "Don't give up!"

While filming the waves, which never does them justice, I turned the camera on myself and apologized for getting the crew into this predicament. After telling my family that I loved them, I put the camera in a watertight case that would float if we went down. Slasher stayed with me in the cockpit, calling out the size and direction of the oncoming waves. It felt better to have him there, partly because there was something I could no longer postpone.

"I'll be back in a bit. I've got to hit the head."

"Now? Are you crazy? Just go in you foul weather gear."

"Deuce, Dude, you need to take the helm."

I went below, placed the plastic container in the Slasher-broken head, and held on. It was like riding a mechanical bull. Satisfied with my decision, I perused a Latitude 38 magazine and took my sweet time.

Thirty minutes later, Slasher had an announcement of his own: "Oh, man, I've got to pee."

"Well, now, that's a totally different thing, isn't it? Take your own advice and go in your foulies. After all, you're already drenched."

☼　⚓　⊙

"Well, I'm certainly not going to stand up and pee overboard." After a long grimace, he started to grin. "Oh, man, that feels better."

We'd been running due south for hours, plumb to the following seas, but we needed to head east to make Bahia Santa Maria. Aside from that, the only other port of refuge for hundreds of miles was Man of War Cove at the entrance to Bahia Magdalena.

The radio chirped to life; there was a scratchy voice.

"Pan-pan, pan-pan, pan-pan. Attention all mariners: the entrance to Man of War Cove is not an option. Repeat. The entrance to Man of War Cove is not an option. Too treacherous. Do not attempt."

"That's not good. If we get blown past Santa Maria, there'll be no protection until Cabo – if we can even make that. We need to start traversing the waves, but there's a greater risk of capsizing if we do."

"We've got to get out of this," Slasher insisted. "Let's give it a try and see how it goes."

Sam concurred, "I agree; let's try."

"Okay, then, let's hope for the best."

To our delight, Marylee surfed the massive waves well, but it required us to square up with each swell so we wouldn't be broadsided. The action on the tiller felt like rowing. The cockpit stayed surprisingly dry with just an occasional spray.

After two hours of solid progress, we passed through a minefield of submerged rocks where the water turned light blue. The ebbing tide and shallow bottom made the waves stand up even higher. Although we'd become desensitized to the madness, the increased danger of the curling breakers was apparent. We didn't have much further to go, though – only twelve more miles to safety.

"If we just keep doing what we're doing, I think we're going to make it."

I spoke too soon. Just then a monstrous wave curled up behind us – twice as big as anything we'd seen. It hovered there, like it was moving in slow motion, before crashing down before Marylee's stern.

☼ ⚓ ◉

The rush of whitewater whipped the boat around and knocked her on her side. As I dangled from the lifelines on the high side, I could see Slasher partially submerged on the low side. After Marylee recovered, the sea stayed eerily calm for several wave periods before the waves started building again.

"That was a rogue wave! Is everyone okay?"

Slasher was drenched. "I'm fine, but I wish I'd worn a wetsuit."

We shook it off and went back to the task at hand. An hour later, Sam spotted the silhouette of a mountain through the mist.

"Land ho!"

Monte San Lazaro was indeed a beautiful sight. The 1,200-foot pinnacle cradles the crescent bay below, shielding it from northerly winds. Although we'd been blown a few miles off course, we were able to motor back as the seas began to settle.

An hour later, we pulled into the anchorage. It seemed like everyone was on deck to greet us, waving as we motored by. Many of them had been monitoring the radio and were concerned about the dozen or so stragglers still at sea. As it turns out, most of the bigger boats outran the weather and had a relatively uneventful passage.

"Marylee, Marylee, Marylee," the radio chimed with the clarity of a nearby boat.

"This is Marylee," Sam responded.

"Welcome to Santa Maria; we're glad to see you guys. We overheard you relaying your position and were concerned. Is everything alright?" the committee boat inquired.

"Yes, we're fine. It was pretty rough out there, but we're safe now. Thanks for your concern; we'll see you at the beach party."

After setting the anchor in the murky water, the three of us convened in the cockpit and huddled for several minutes. Funny thing about cheating death, it leaves you exhausted and in a state of shock. We pulled off our foulies, hung them over the boom to dry, and collapsed in a heap of salt and sweat.

We woke up a few hours later and prepared a pancake, bacon, and margarita brunch that we all agreed was the best meal we'd ever eaten.

☼   🏃   ◉

Reflecting back on the experience, we'd braved the harshest conditions in the event's history aboard the smallest boat allowed. There was no one to blame – the sea can be a fickle bitch.

> *I still get chills every time I think about those walls of water rising around me. It was such a beautiful sight. That said, I hope to never see anything that beautiful again.*

"All I can say is that when facing death, at least I had the common decency not to soil my armor. Slasher, on the other hand, was so scared he pissed himself rotten."

☼   🏃   ☉

Chapter 10
The Beach Party

The windswept bay held a fleet of grateful cruisers. The blustery conditions made the dinghy landings treacherous in the pounding surf, even in the lee.

Humbled and exhausted, we were content to stay aboard Marylee all morning – discussing the storm we'd just survived. It prompted frank discussions about the risks and rewards of going to sea. Eventually, every sailor is forced to confront adverse conditions; it literally comes with the territory.

We felt better after a few cocktails. At some point, we became more interested in celebrating life than contemplating death – so we went to the party. We landed the dinghy in front of a fish camp in the shadow of the towering granite peak. In a large palapa on a barren bluff, some local chefs sautéed butterflied lobster tails on a massive griddle. From our vantage point there, the fleet of dinghies leaving their boats looked like parachutists jumping from planes. When a local rock band began to play, Slasher, an accomplished drummer in a BC band, took over the skins and played late into the evening.

At one point, I left the party and went on a walk by myself to the windward side of the peninsula to see if the storm had subsided. It hadn't. I sat on the beach, with the sand stinging my ankles, trying to muster the courage to go back to sea the next day.

Chapter 11
The Final Leg

"The tip of the Cape at San Lucas, with the huge gray Friars standing up on end, has behind the rocks a little beach which is a small boy's dream of pirates."
- John Steinbeck, Log from the Sea of Cortez

Mornings in Baja are magnificent – and this one was no exception. The colorful fleet continued south on the final leg in greatly improved conditions. Marylee rode the diminishing swells effortlessly as Otto manned the helm.

I made a toast to the tranquil weather and building high pressure. "Here's to mellow conditions; perfect will just have to do."

"If it stays like this, let's just keep sailing," Sam giggled. "I love it out here."

Slasher and Pinky

Slasher had other ideas. "Not me; I'm ready to get off this boat and do some slashing." "Sorry Pinky," he said to his spank toy under the dodger, "I'm trading you in for a hottie with a hotel room."

He and I fished for most of the day. Although we each had a pole, we preferred the meat hook. I still remember the advice from the old salt who sold it to me:

> *"If you want to fish, use a pole.*
> *If you want to eat, use a meat hook."*

A meat hook is simply a thick line with a big hook that uses the sailboat winches as reels. The fish has no chance against the mechanical advantage and is easily landed, despite its size.

When you do land a big one, most cruisers like to hang it from the boom by the tail and bleed it overboard. The wise fisherman will put the fish in a 5-gallon bucket with holes drilled in the bottom to guard it from sharks. Dangling a bleeding fish above the water without protection is a good way to lose half of your fish.

That evening, under a balmy, starlit sky, we crossed the Tropic of Cancer. There's something special that happens at latitude 23°30', where hard-fought voyages begin to feel like vacations. Sam and I sat on the foredeck at dawn and watched the puffy white clouds roll by.

After rounding Cabo Falso, we saw our destination in the distance. Bat rays jumped high out of the water, flapping their wings in a lame attempt to stay airborne. Curious little bastards hover at the top momentarily, with their beady eyes fixed on you, before belly-flopping back in.

I uncorked a bottle of wine that I'd been saving to commemorate the special occasion. We danced around the deck in the afternoon sun as Marylee ghosted past the iconic arch that framed the finish line.

"This is top living," Sam said as she dangled her feet off the bow. "It just doesn't get any better than this."

"It's hard to believe that just a few days ago we thought we were goners. My, how things can change in such a short amount of time."

☼   ⚲   ⊛

"Yeah, just like the weather," Slasher teased.

The bay was packed with beaches, resorts, and parasails. After nine days on a small boat, reaching Cabo meant more than just an accomplishment; it meant hot showers, fresh food, and some well-earned rest.

The smiling faces of inebriated Ha-Ha-ers greeted us as we pulled into our slip. An hour later, we were partying in a roofless bar with most of them. Bone tired, we meandered back to the boat at an early hour and fell fast asleep   impervious to the thumping nightclubs that encircle the marina.

We slept like mummies in our fiberglass sarcophagus until the temperature below became unbearable. As we were having morning coffee in the cockpit, I felt noticeably more relaxed than I'd been in months.

"Tell you what, I'm happy not being a captain right now. It's so nice to have Marylee tied up in a slip."

"Not me, I'm ready to get back out there once Slasher leaves. After that last leg, I'm hooked."

At brunch in a palapa café with a mariachi band playing in the distance, Slasher fell madly in love with our waitress. "Watch me dazzle her with my tales of the sea; she'll melt like butter in my brave arms."

Unfortunately, she didn't.

Later on, we dinghied over to Lover's Beach. It's a great place to snorkel, where the nutrient-rich Pacific meets the tropical Sea of Cortez. The dense schools of angelfish there can envelop you so completely that it can be disorienting.

On a secluded shore, strewn with seashells, we were sipping Por qué no's.

"This adventure makes me appreciate life even more," Sam said. "I feel so fortunate to be here – like I've done something really important."

"Me too, Sammi, and our journey has just begun."

☼   ⚓   ◉

As we motored back into the marina, tiny Marylee looked silly among the megayachts surrounding her. Their dinghies were bigger than her – and some even had helicopters.

Cabo had boomed in recent years, attracting a great deal of wealth and tourism. Now it stews in its own decadent juices, making Vegas feel wholesome. Packed with gringos drinking "hair of the dog" tequila sunrises, Cabo will give you a hangover even if you don't drink alcohol.

Come Sunday, these depleted souls will sulk through Los Cabos International Airport, looking several years older than they did when they arrived. Sunburned, hungover, wearing big-ass sombreros from their favorite bars – if they don't keep drinking, remorse will set in.

After the Baja Ha-Ha awards ceremony, where we were recognized for being the smallest boat in the fleet, we exchanged "boat cards" with dozens of our newfound friends that we hoped to see down the road – including a lady that was knocked unconscious by a flying fish on a night watch.

When it was time for Slasher to leave the next morning to catch a flight to cold and rainy Canada, we huddled for a group hug in the cockpit. After disembarking, he rolled his rigid suitcase down the dock and out of sight.

Click, click, click

I turned to Sam and said, "I'm gonna miss that cabin boy, but I'm sure not gonna miss his bulky luggage."

☼   🏃   ◉

Chapter 12
Misery Loves Company

Marina Cabo San Lucas is one of the most expensive in the world – catering primarily to megayacht and sportfishing clientele. Many of the boats there are continuously polished masterpieces.

"They charged me more to park my boat here for the next five years than the boat is worth," one owner told me, "in cash upfront."

The high fees motivated us to move Marylee to La Paz before we flew home for the holidays. Although we enjoyed cruising the Cabo area, the nonstop nightclub scene had us longing for peace and quiet. Rich in history and fascinating to explore, La Paz is a gateway to some of Mexico's finest cruising grounds and is known for having reasonably priced marinas. We spent a couple of days preparing for a trip around the peninsula.

"This looks pretty straight forward," I said, looking at a chart of Southern Baja. "We could probably make it to La Paz in three or four days if we needed to."

Sam peered up from under the brim of her crumpled straw hat and replied, "According to this cruising guide, it's only 148 nautical miles. That's nothing; we almost sailed that far each day down the coast."

"That's true, but now that Slasher is gone, I'd rather sail during daylight hours as much as possible. We're not in a hurry, so let's take our time and enjoy the trip."

Indeed, the distance seemed insignificant compared to the massive stretch of the mighty Pacific we'd just traversed. Plus there are numerous anchorages around the East Cape to explore, two of which are considered to have outstanding protection: Los Frailes and Bahia de Los Muertos, or "Bay of the Dead," recently renamed "Bay of Dreams" by some savvy developers.

From there, we'd just chug up the Cerralvo and San Lorenzo Channels, and we'd be in Bahia La Paz. The weather in Cabo was clear and calm, and Marina La Paz, on the other side, was reporting similar conditions.

We pushed away from the dock at dawn, upon a sea of silhouetted seagulls. There was a floral scent in the air from the gardens and golf courses that lined the verdant shore. Mexico was slowly waking up.

We motored past the luxury resorts carved into red-rock cliffs and sandy arroyos that flash flood when it rains in the looming Laguna Mountains.

"This is your captain speaking; we should be landing in Los Frailes in three hours." "Please sit back and enjoy the ride."

Just then, the radio chirped to life…

We overheard a conversation between two boats: "We're having some real trouble here. We've got green water over the bow, thirty knots of wind on our nose, and a broken belt on our water pump that's causing the engine to overheat. I doubt we can make it to Los Frailes without an engine, but Michael's too seasick to fix it right now. I'll keep you updated on our progress. Bright Angel out."

"Hmm, that's odd; the weather sure is beautiful here. I wonder if they're in the middle of the Sea, coming from Mazatlan. It can be calm on both sides and howl in the middle. Based on the clarity of their radio signal, they're within fifteen miles of us," I estimated.

Sam hailed them on the VHF, "Bright Angel, Bright Angel, Bright Angel, this is sailing vessel Marylee."

"Marylee, this is Bright Angel. Go ahead."

"We overheard your last transmission. Just wondering where you are and if you need any assistance?"

"Hi Marylee, we're two miles off Punta Gorda and not making any headway in this mess. We left Cabo last night and are trying to make Los Frailes. No assistance is needed presently, but thanks for asking."

"Honey, they're directly in front of us," Sam said, pointing to their position on the chart, "and they left hours before us." "Guess we better batten down the hatches."

☼ ⚓ ◉

It was hard to believe the weather could turn nasty when the conditions were so serene. Keenly aware that the most reliable marine forecast comes from the vessel directly in front of you – we braced for a gale in near perfect sailing conditions.

Good thing we did; just as we rounded Punta Gorda, the winds and the waves began buffeting Marylee's bow. They were sinister square blocks of water that reduced the hull speed to a crawl. Marylee shuddered as she punched through their faces; her decks were drenched with heavy spray.

Skippers go to great lengths to minimize the wear and tear on their vessels. Breakage can be expensive to fix, especially in remote places, and it can be dangerous if it disables the boat at sea. Having been spoiled with downwind sailing conditions since San Diego, the uphill slog seemed exceptionally bogus. As the waves grew larger, and the wind blew harder – we decided to turn around.

"Let's go back a few miles, to where it's pleasant, and try again later tonight. The tides will be more favorable, and hopefully the winds will have diminished too."

We retreated back to Punta Palmilla, a manicured resort with a crescent-shaped cove, where we snorkeled and played bocce ball in the calm conditions. At dusk, we dined by candlelight under the clear desert skies.

We weighed anchor at midnight – determined to give it another try. To our delight, conditions had improved significantly. The flooding tide pushed us in the right direction, and the winds had shifted to put us on a beam reach – a fine angle of sail. Off in the distance, we spotted a string of white lights – the masthead anchor lights of the fleet at Los Frailes. It was nice to see so many boats anchored behind the giant white rock; we knew we'd have friends there.

We dropped our hook beside a stout Hans Christensen 33 named Melani. Exhausted from the long day, we vowed to sleep-in…but that didn't happen. By sunrise, every skipper, including me, was on deck inspecting their ground tackle and making adjustments in the gale-force conditions.

Four days went by. Four days of relentless northerlies coming from the direction we all needed to go – and where was Bright Angel? Unable to make Frailes under sail, we assumed they either set a stormy course to Mazatlan, or retreated back to Cabo. It wasn't until we met up with them several months later that we heard about their harrowing passage. Engineless on a dark, colliding sea, they were seasick, scared, and all alone out there. It took them two hellish days to make Mazatlan.

I repeated the same thing each morning: "Hopefully the weather will break today; we need to make some forward progress."

It never did...

We attempted the forty-seven mile passage to Los Muertos twice at midnight, faring poorly on both occasions. The viciously sharp eight-foot seas made for a wet and scary ride. Down below, our possessions were ejected from the lockers and splayed onto the cabin floor – tossed around like a Mongolian stir-fry. We made the decision to retreat back to Los Frailes after all forward progress was lost.

On our heroic second attempt, we were within ten miles of our destination before being forced to turn around after the electrical distribution panel tore from its mounts. We couldn't push Marylee any further until we made repairs.

Our boat's small size wasn't the culprit; dozens of larger vessels, including megayachts, returned to Frailes each morning battered, humbled, and wishing they'd never left. There was no forward progress regardless of waterline.

The trapped fleet was making the most of it, though. We spent the days reading, playing board games, fishing, and mingling with the other cruisers. Our friends Chay, Katie, and 5-year-old Jamie on Esprit arrived with some freshly caught Wahoo that we traded for some frosty cold beers and a pack of tortillas.

"These are the coldest beers we've had in months," Chay remarked as they buzzed away in their dinghy.

⚓ ⚓ ⊙

"That's because we have an icebox instead of a refrigerator," I hollered back, "they won't be cold much longer."

By the end of the following week, feeling pinched by the lack of progress, we concluded that cruisers should never be on a schedule.

Sam seemed discouraged: "At this point, we don't have much choice. If we don't head back to Cabo now, we'll probably miss our flight home for the holidays."

She was right. We still had two sizable passages to reach La Paz, and the opposing winds were relentless. Although returning to Cabo wasn't ideal, it was our best option at the time. In sailing, where you intend to go and where you actually go are only sometimes the same place.

On a northbound flight a few days later, we spotted Los Frailes from the plane. The sea still looked choppy, and the fleet hadn't moved. Our minds were at ease with Marylee safely in a slip, though; retreating was the right decision.

☼ ⚲ ☉

Chapter 13
Chumming for Coffee Pots

T he holidays are a special time for my family; otherwise, I would have continued cruising. We spent each Christmas at my parent's cabin in the backwoods of Maine – a winter wonderland most years. We'd toboggan down the snowy hill behind the house, stopping occasionally for cookies and hot chocolate. Maine at Christmas is like living in a Norman Rockwell painting – the antithesis of Cabo San Lucas.

On our flight back to Los Cabos in early January, I reviewed the list of projects I needed to do on Marylee. First and foremost was to fix the Slasher-broken head with the replacement parts I had packed in my luggage.

"Here's an idea; let's tune out the media while we're cruising. If we see a newspaper in a market, let's agree that we can only read the front page. If it's not on the front page, we probably don't need to know about it."

"Agreed!" Sam giggled. "Nothing's going to bring us down."

On the taxi ride from the airport, we gawked at two wrecked yachts resting on the beach near a bar named *"The Office."* Apparently, an unexpected south swell struck the anchorage with fifteen-foot breaking waves. Every skipper was scrambling to get their boats into deeper water; apparently some weren't fast enough. The sad sight of those salvage boats sent chills down our spines. It was a reminder of how precarious our life at sea would be.

Although Cabo San Lucas isn't our favorite place in Mexico, it's great for provisioning for a long voyage. There's even a big box store where we purchased massive amounts of provisions, including a bag of frozen chicken wings that we'd have to eat "muy pronto" since we didn't have a freezer. We filled Marylee's holds with foodstuffs in case we got stuck at Los Frailes again.

From there, we decided to cross the Sea of Cortez to the mainland and head south to the Mexican Riviera for the winter. It would be warmer than La Paz that time of year, and most of the Ha-Ha-ers were already there. In order to make the crossing, though, we'd have to wait for a weather window to open – and who knows how long that would take?

It felt wonderful to be back in the balmy tropics after snowy Maine. We sailed back to Los Frailes and anchored next to a crusty old hippie from Telluride aboard a nameless yellow sloop. He dinghied over to us, tied up to Marylee, and opened a ratty knapsack full of paperback books.

"You guys interested in trading some books, man? I've read all these like five times."

"Uh, actually, we haven't read any of ours yet. Most of them are Christmas presents, so we don't have any to trade right now."

"Aw, come on, man. If you could trade a few, I'd really appreciate it."

"Well, I guess we can trade a couple…"

"Thanks, brother. You guys are cool. Where're you headed?"

"Mazatlan, either tomorrow or the day after, depending on the weather," Sam said, as she gathered our new books to exchange for his grungy ones.

"You better go tomorrow, man; in two days something's coming," he said, like a half-crazed seer.

"What's coming? The weather models seem pretty benign."

"Trust me, man, something's coming. Nothing was forecast last week – and in a matter of minutes, we had huge waves breaking in here."

"Yeah, we heard about that – and saw a couple wrecked boats on the beach in Cabo. I guess everyone was caught off guard."

"Yeah, man. I almost lost her. My engine wouldn't start, and I couldn't reach my anchor with the waves breaking on the bow. So, I just went down below and hoped for the best. When I woke up the next morning, she was hanging on two threads of rope, man. Just two threads!"

Sam gasped, "Oh my gosh, that's really scary. Have you considered switching to an all-chain rode? There are so many sharp rocks around here."

"That's a good idea; I should get some chain," he mumbled.

☼ ⚲ ☉

"What about you? Where're you headed?" I asked.

"Um, I'll probably stay here for a few more months, you know, and get to know the place."

"Wow, that's a long time to stay in one anchorage."

"Not for me, man. I stayed in Mag Bay for like five months last year before the harbormaster finally kicked me out."

"Well, we'll probably leave in the morning then. It was nice meeting you."

"Right on. You'll be fine if you leave tomorrow. Give that Racor [fuel filter] a tap and get out there," he said as he sputtered away.

We watched him spend the rest of the afternoon fishing for his dinner. Sam peered at him through the binoculars.

"Boy, that guy is hardcore. Talk about living off the grid."

"Yeah, he's a modern-day hunter-gatherer – and probably a damn good fisherman."

Later that afternoon, we were lounging in the cockpit, eating chicken wings, and playing dice games. Sam started tossing her bones overboard instead of in the garbage.

"Why keep greasy bones onboard?" she reasoned. "Chickens are biodegradable, aren't they?"

It made sense at the time; after all, garbage ripens quickly in the tropics – so I started throwing mine overboard as well. Before long, the water was boiling with fish fighting for the crumbs floating on the surface.

After we finished eating, Sam went below to brew a pot of coffee for the next morning. It was easier to make it while the boat was at anchor, and making it the night before meant not having to hassle with it in the morning. After pouring the brew in a Thermos, she leaned over the side of the boat to rinse out the coffee grounds – a recipe for disaster.

Although we enjoyed washing our dishes in the sea because it conserved freshwater and left a pleasant, salty, nutty taste on them, Marylee's high freeboard meant you'd have to lean your body way over to reach the water. For that reason we usually washed them from the dinghy; but it was already deflated and stowed for the passage.

☼ ⚚ ☉

Thump. Scream. Splash.

Sam giggled as she climbed up the swim ladder. Once back onboard, she went directly for the dive locker, grabbed my snorkel gear, and handed it to me.

"What's this for?" I asked.

"Some percolator parts fell overboard. You've got to dive down and get them before it gets any darker; otherwise, we won't be able to make anymore coffee. Go rescue our coffeepot, sailor boy."

Diving at dusk did not sound appealing, but she reassured me that it would be easy to find such shiny objects in only thirty feet of water. I had no choice but to try. I jumped in the murky water, switched on my underwater flashlight, took a deep breath, and swam toward the bottom.

As I was diving down, a large shark passed beneath me. I remembered the chicken wings – those damn chicken wings – and shot out of the water screaming, "SHARK, CHICKEN WINGS, SHARK!"

I scrambled back aboard, panting and dripping like a wet dog. Sam sat down beside me, wrapped a towel around me, and said, "That's okay, Honey; at least we have plenty of tea."

Chapter 14
The Pie-o-neer

W

e were delighted to learn that the green and white Pacific Seacraft 37 anchored next to us was leaving for Mazatlan the next morning too. We agreed to be "buddy boats."

At dawn, Marylee and Kaleidoscope were lifted to sea by twenty knots of glorious wind. Our course would take us 168 nautical miles across the Sea of Cortez to the Mexican mainland. It's a notoriously treacherous passage because it's where the large swells of the Pacific collide with the short-interval square waves of the Sea of Cortez. The result can be confused seas that simultaneously slam the boat from multiple directions. If not properly timed, it can be as agitated as a washing machine in the middle.

The stars were epic that evening. The dry desert air and lack of pollution really bring them out. Through the pitch blackness of a moonless night, we could see the faint glow of Mazatlan from a hundred miles away. After twenty-six hours of smooth sailing, we coasted into Marina Mazatlan and tied up just after sunrise.

Mornings are a good time to make landfall because conditions are usually calm with good visibility. A prudent skipper will not enter an unfamiliar harbor at night; rather, they'll stay in a holding pattern offshore until daybreak. Even if you know the waters well, things can change since the last time you were there.

Mazatlan is a fine place for cruisers – it's relatively inexpensive and has plenty of marinas and boat repair facilities. It's a traditional Mexican city that hasn't been overrun by tourists. It feels manageable, simple, and Mexican.

We found ourselves slipping into a smooth Latin groove there. We stayed out late every night exploring the town, eating street tacos, and making new friends in cantinas. It was the perfect place to decompress from a fast-paced American lifestyle – something that typically takes months.

We decided to go on a land excursion. Initially we wanted to go up the Copper Canyon on a train, but decided against it when we heard about the heavy snowfall on the rim. Instead, we decided to take a bus to the historic silver mining town of Copala – high in the foothills of the Sierra Madre Occidental Mountains.

"When you go there, get some pie at Daniel's; it's very famous," advised Sylvia, the effervescent Marina Manager.

In Mexico, there are two classes of bus service: the modern air-conditioned bus with drapes and cushy seats or the ratty old "chicken bus" for half the fare. Most cruisers, including us, preferred taking the chicken bus because it was a much more interesting experience, and yes, there's an occasional chicken onboard. Despite the exhaust fumes, lack of air conditioning, and bumpy ride, every trip is an adventure.

Our bus creaked up the mountain switchbacks, grinding gears each time the driver shifted. Eventually he pulled off at a gravel turn-out and shouted, "Copala!"

We didn't see a village, but he assured us the trail into the forest would lead us to one. After a brief hike past chicken coops and pigpens, we reached the cobblestone streets of Copala, poignantly situated atop a blooming bluff. It's a sleepy pueblo with a western feel, tidied up for tourists. The streets were empty except for a boy and his donkey in front of a stone church covered in bougainvillea.

"You want me to take your picture, señor?"

"¿Por qué no?"

After chuckling to myself at the inside joke, I handed him my camera and posed with Sam and the donkey.

"What's your burro's name?" Sam asked.

"George Bush."

After working up an appetite exploring abandoned silver mines, Sam had pie on her mind: "Let's get a slice, I'm starving."

Upon finding Daniel's Hotel and Restaurant, I held the ornately carved door open for her.

"Entrevue."

We were immediately greeted by a fair-skinned man with a flowing white beard and sky-blue eyes; "Hi, I'm Daniel. Welcome to Copala. What brings you guys all the way up here?"

"Your pie," Sam giggled, "so it better be good, Buster. We took a chicken bus all the way from Mazatlan to get some."

"Oh it is. You won't be disappointed. People come from all over to get a slice. Do you guys need a room too? Since you came all this way, I'll give you a big discount."

"Hmm, what do you think, Sammi? It might be a nice break from the boat."

"Oh my gosh, that would be fantastic; I'd rather not spend two more hours on a bus today."

We decided to stay, but it took a long time to get a room key. It was refreshing to meet someone with absolutely no sense of urgency.

"After you're settled in, come down for some pie; it's on the house."

The cold-white-concrete stairway led to a cold-white-concrete hallway that took us to our cold-white-concrete room.

Sam's teeth were chattering; "This place is frickin' freezing. It's like being in an igloo."

We set our things down and went back outside before hypothermia set in. Daniel was on the patio in a rocking chair with a blanket across his lap and a Panama hat on his head.

"Care to join me? These are the best seats in the house."

We spent the remainder of the afternoon rocking with Daniel, washing down pie with Por qué no's and watching the sun set over the papaya plantations in the valley below.

He told us about coming to Copala thirty years prior after his mother fell ill. Although she'd met and married Daniel's Scandinavian father in California, she returned to her hometown of Copala after he passed away. Daniel fell in love with the area and decided to move there too.

"So how did you become such a famous pie guy?" Sam asked.

☼   ⚹   ⊙

He chuckled then replied, "Well, my mom kept complaining that my restaurant didn't have any desserts, so she started making pies from her grandmother's recipe. Next thing we knew, some travel magazines discovered it, then they turned some cruise ships onto it, and the rest is history."

Daniel explained that successful things in Mexico are often copied – and his pie was no exception. After it started attracting large amounts of tourists, the other restaurants in the town started serving coconut-banana-cream pie, too.

He spoke of his traitorous former employees: "They double-crossed me and gave Granny's recipe to the competition."

As a matter of fact, every restaurant in town had a pie painted on it. One even had the nerve to write "BEST PIE IN TOWN!" across the front in capital letters.

I suggested that Daniel challenge them to a pie fight on the cobblestone streets at high noon. Pies-a-flying. As whimsical as it was, there's only one flavor of pie served in Copala – Daniel's coconut-banana-creamed variety. And although he and his mother were pie-o-neers of sorts, the only thing that distinguished him from his competitors were the words: "*The original coconut-banana-cream pie*" painted in cursive above his doorway. Other than that, he's just another coconut-banana-creamed pie vendor in the coconut-banana-creamed hills of Sinaloa, Mexico.

Chapter 15
The Stowaway

S ailing south past Mazatlan at sunset, we saw the elusive green flash as the sun dipped below the horizon. As we passed the Pacifico Brewery, I held up a bottle. On its label is an image of an ocean rock beside the brewery, as seen from the water. Whenever I drink that beer, I am reminded of that moment.

The forecast called for favorable winds, clear skies, and a full moon. Winter is a wonderful season in the Mexican tropics – with puffy white clouds that stay white all night long. Sunrises and sunsets are particularly spectacular at that latitude, and no one appreciates them more than cruisers. Immersed in nature, rising and resting with the sun, their biorhythms become in sync with the natural light.

Later that evening, moving south at seven knots with a favorable tide, Marylee danced across the moon-drenched sea. It was an eighty-five mile passage to Isla Isabella – an extinct volcano forty miles off the Mexican mainland. Coined the "Mexican Galapagos" by Jacques Cousteau, the wildlife on the island is extraordinary.

The skies darkened from millions of seabirds circling overhead as we drew near. It was comical to see exhausted ones resting on the backs of sea turtles as they floated on the surface. There were so many Gray whales around us, mating and slamming their fins on the water, that we feared hitting one. Dolphins and frigates escorted us into the shallows of this magical prehistoric world.

Sadly, the swells were too big for us to anchor safely, so after circling the island, we begrudgingly set course for San Blas. We vowed to return to Isabella when the sea-state was more settled.

We rounded Punta Camarones and entered Bahia Mantanchen at twilight, with silhouettes of coconut palms swaying against the peach-colored sky. The fragrant air, lush mountains, and cascading waterfalls of our first jungle anchorage were reminiscent of the north shore of Kauai.

☼   ⚓   ☉

A perfect week went by – and we were relishing the cruising lifestyle. We ate Mariscos in thatched-palapa restaurants, played bocce ball on pristine beaches, and napped in hammocks tied between palms. One afternoon, we took a jungle cruise into the mangroves to a popular freshwater swimming hole known as Tovara Springs – where a harmless resident crocodile named Felipe suns on the bank next to the swimmers.

Except for the "no-see-um" gnats that come out at sunrise and sunset, where the jungle meets the sea, there was no negativity. It's hard to believe such a small creature could have such a painful bite.

We met a bright-eyed 8-year-old boy named Carlos there who worked in his family's restaurant. He was a sweet child who took great pride in being an attentive waiter. One evening after dinner, I gifted him a keychain, small pocketknife, and flashlight from the bag of trinkets I brought along to hand out to special people along the way. There was a moment of hesitation, like he wasn't sure if I was being serious, then he snatched them up and ran inside to show his mother his treasures.

The next day, we motored Marylee to the fuel dock in nearby San Blas. Just after filling her up and pushing her away, a ponga with six Mexican Navy soldiers with machine guns and a drug-sniffing dog pulled alongside us. They looked serious.

Apparently, San Blas is a major drug smuggling port, and contraband is often loaded from the fuel dock. Not surprising, since it's home turf for the Sinaloa cartel. Thankfully, they never boarded us; they just glanced at our passports and paperwork. But it didn't matter, though; they'd never find my weed.

Early the next morning, as I was preparing the cockpit for departure, we had a rude awakening.

"Oh my gosh! Get back inside, right now!" Sam insisted.

"Why, what's wrong?"

"Just get down here!"

Her tone had me moving quickly. Once inside, she spun me around and pointed at a large snake wrapped around our propane tank on the transom – just behind where I was standing.

☼ 🕏 ◉

"Hey, it's a boa constrictor," I said with some certainty. "They make great pets; can we keep him?"

Sam wasn't amused but was empathetic. "Aw, it must have been exhausted and climbed up there to rest."

"I'll take care of this."

I slithered out of the forward hatch while Sam filmed the encounter. Sensing my approach, the stowaway raised its head and flicked its tongue toward me.

Stowaway Snake

"Be careful, Honey, it might be poisonous."

"No worries, mate. Crocodile Dandee is going to remove the snake from our boat. Crikey, he's a big bugger," I said, prying it with a boat hook.

Sam spoke anxiously; her exact words were, "Yeah, Honey, just please be very careful. Don't even. Babe, just be careful. Ah, geez-Louise, it's big."

Little by little, the five-foot snake was extended to a point of no return and fell into the water.

⚓ 𝑋 ⊙

As soon as Sam climbed up into the cockpit, I pointed down beside her and shouted, "There's another one!"

She jumped three feet… straight up.

Our friend, John, on the trawler anchored next to us, was filming the whole ordeal too. To his chagrin, as soon as the snake hit the water, it raised its head and swam directly for his boat. Had a banjo been picking in the background, it would have been the perfect slapstick comedy. The snake assaulted his boat from every point possible – first up the dinghy, then the transom, and later the anchor chain.

John thwarted each boarding with his boat hook. At one point the snake coiled around it, and John pulled it completely out of the water. Discouraged and with a throbbing headache, it finally gave up and swam back into the mangroves.

Reflecting on how the snake gained purchase, it was the Nor'Sea's outboard rudder that was to blame. It's a great feature, though, because it allows singlehanded sailors to climb back on board if they fall off. The movie *"Open Water 2: Adrift"* is a stark reminder of what can happen on boats without this feature if the crew jumps in the water without lowering the swim ladder first.

When I went to the bow to weigh anchor, I noticed Carlos waving at us in the distance. We dinghied over to see what he wanted. With tears running down his face because he was sad to see us go, he handed me a fine bottle of tequila and gave Sam a long hug.

Chapter 16
The Port Captain

C hacala is a special place. At the end of a floral cove, there's a
     sugar-white beach rimmed with coconut palms and dense groves
     of papaya. On the mountainous south side, there's a retreat and
wellness center with numerous hiking trails, and to the north, there's a
gated development with mansions.

We slipped into the anchorage after a short sail down the rugged
coast. Since it was considered a working port and we'd be there overnight,
we were required to check in with the Port Captain's office on the hill.

The process of checking in and out of each port was compulsory
until 2006, when it was replaced with an all-Mexico cruising permit.

It was a cumbersome process that required us to:

- Present our documents to the Port Captain so the
  officials could complete the entry paperwork.
- Find a bank and pay a fee.
- Find a copy center and make copies of everything.
- Return all the documentation to the Port Captain's
  office.
- Check-out prior to leaving.

Between holidays, limited office hours, and the scarcity of banks
and copy centers, one night at anchor could require multiple days of
paperwork. And because the Port Captain received revenue from the
process, they kept a watchful eye out for violators.

"Sounds like the Port Captain here is pretty laid-back," Sam said
as she read from a cruising guide. "It says here that you can usually find
him asleep in a hammock in front of his office."

I liked him already.

Instead, we found him standing at attention on the balcony, dressed in a pressed white uniform, proudly presiding over his harbor.

"Hola Capitano, ese es mi velero allí," I said, pointing down at Marylee.

He replied in perfect English, "I know, I've been admiring your beautiful little boat ever since you arrived."

A fellow man of the sea, he was intrigued by our adventure. He commended us for traveling so far on such a small boat. As we started to sit down at his desk to complete the paperwork, he insisted I try his chair. As soon as I did, he spun it around to face the window overlooking the bay.

"Tranquilo," he said softly, "muy tranquilo."

Indeed, it was a vision of paradise – and he was a man who truly appreciated his job. Having paid his dues in the busy ports of Ixtapa, Manzanillo, and Puerto Vallarta, he was happy to be in his sleepy little port where nothing ever happened.

We spent four blissful days there, just enough time for Chacala to fully soak in. We ate most meals on the beach, where we could watch Marylee sway in the distance. I loved seeing her there.

There was only "un problema" with Chacala... the wretched smell. You see, each morning, two putrid shrimp boats would return from fishing and anchor directly upwind of us. They reeked so badly that we were driven from our boat. We nicknamed them "U.S.S. Stinky" and "H.M.S. Sir-Stinks-a-lot" for the fishy odor they wafted around paradise. If it weren't for the smell, we could have stayed there forever.

☼　ⵜ　☉

Chapter 17
Paradise Found

With provisions running low, we were eager to reach a luxury resort and marina near Puerto Vallarta known as Paradise Village. After several weeks of cruising, we relished the thought of rinsing the accumulated salt off our boat and bodies and relaxing poolside with umbrella drinks. After a pleasant sail straddling the cliffs around Sayulita, we rounded Punta de Mita and dropped our anchor at dusk. Anxious to be pampered, we made the final push to "Paradise" at daybreak.

It was a spectacularly beautiful morning, with numerous whales breeching in the fog-strewn distance. Marylee knifed through the soft, humid air quietly under sail. Suddenly, a humpback whale jumped out of the water beside us, less than a boat-length away, spraying us with a concussive splash.

Sam cheered, "Oh my gosh, that was incredible! Did you see him looking directly at us? He was checking us out."

"How could I miss it? His eye was the size of a basketball."

A few minutes later, some bottlenose dolphins began jumping our bow as we approached the marina. I joked that the resort probably trained them to escort us to our slip.

"Are we supposed to tip 'em? Do they expect us to throw them a fish?"

After passing through the churning breakwater between the rock jetties, we slipped into a quiet estuarial lagoon adjacent to the marina. We pulled into our slip directly in front of the yacht club. Once the boat was secure, we embraced. It was so nice to be tied up after so many weeks on the hook.

"Welcome to Paradise," I said to Sam. "We finally made it."

Indeed, the lavish amenities were a welcome change of pace. There were hot tubs, pools, showers, restaurants, tennis courts, and internet

☼   🏃   ⊙

cafés. There was even a golf course, zoo, spa, supermarket stocked with American goods, and bikes we could use for free.

On par with many Hawaiian resorts, Paradise Village is a five-star oasis for cruisers. It's a great place to take care of personal business and unwind. Most people envision cruising as a relatively stress-free lifestyle, but it's anything but. The ever-daunting duties and responsibilities of being a captain are consuming, so it was nice to take a break. Let it blow, baby, let it blow. And because of her dainty size, Marylee costs about as much as a cheeseburger at the pool bar to dock there each night.

Our slip in front of the Vallarta Yacht Club was a particularly social one. Several people came down the dock to welcome us and admire our little sailboat that had come so far. Among them were friends we'd met along the way, making our arrival feel like a homecoming. Naturally, it turned into an impromptu dock party.

¿Por qué no?

Once the crowd dispersed, we took long, hot showers before giving Marylee one. Scrubbed, polished, and waxed – she glistened in the tropical sun. After months of living aboard, she'd become a refined little cruiser. More than a boat to us now; we considered her a friend.

Over the next couple of days, we attended to personal matters, including banking, taxes, and responding to emails. We hadn't received them in weeks. It was comforting to see that Violet was paying rent and sending courteous notes about how much she was enjoying the property – though it was odd that the payments were being made with $500 cash cards. I was having too much fun to give it much thought.

Without a care in the world, we ate countless club sandwiches poolside. We made a lot of cruiser friends there, including several families. The resort is well equipped for kids with an abundance of outdoor activities. When they weren't being home-schooled, they were swimming in the numerous pools, boogie-boarding on the beach, or fishing from dinghies.

☼ ⚓ ◉

The combination of learning about other cultures, spending quality time with their families, and experiencing the wonders of the sea exposes them to things they'd never be taught in school. It's no surprise that when they return to conventional classrooms, most cruiser kids are far ahead of their peers in terms of academics and maturity. Most speak several languages, understand weather patterns, and have driven boats across oceans long before they're allowed to drive a car.

In places like Tentacatita, south of Puerto Vallarta, large groups of families congregate for seasons. By midwinter, the anchorage becomes part summer camp and part school – where each boat teaches a different subject.

5-year-old Jaime from Esprit was one of our favorites. After his morning studies, he'd sail his little dinghy around the marina by himself. Without video games, television, or other distractions, this little buccaneer immersed himself in wholesome play.

His parents remarked about the effect cruising had on him at Christmas. Having been away from advertising, there were only three things on his letter to Santa that year, down from a dozen the year before. They were practical things too – a fishing pole, a tackle box, and a new boogie board.

One afternoon there was a rap on Marylee's hull. It was Jamie delivering a green card with "Happy St. Patrick's Day" written in crooked crayon, and a leprechaun drawn on the front of it.

"Wait here a moment," I told him, "I have something for you too."

After shuffling through the locker below, I handed him Slasher's Grim Reaper mask – left over from Halloween. He put the oversized mask on and ran down the dock – terrorizing anyone unfortunate enough to be in his path.

"He's lucky to be adventuring with his family at such a young age," Sam said to his mother, Katie.

"We totally agree," she replied. "The quality of life out here is incredible – and there are a lot more families cruising than we expected. We've met so many interesting people with wonderful children so far."

☼ ⚱ ◉

"Well, the apple doesn't fall far from the tree," I reasoned. "Adventurous parents inspire adventurous children."

More than a decade later, the McWilliam family completed their journey around the world. After so many years of sailing, Jamie stepped off Esprit to attend college. Other than a terrifying encounter with Somali pirates, where their friends from Santa Barbara were attacked and killed on a boat a few miles in front of them, it was a profoundly positive experience.

On another boat, appropriately named Monkey Girl, ten-year-old Annika loved to swing from the ropes of her tall-masted ketch. She'd swing between the masts for hours at a time.

"I like it best when we're underway," Annika cheered. "It's more fun when the boat's really moving around."

Chapter 18
High Tension on No Worries

When our friends Rick and Holly reaffirmed their decision to make the passage to the South Pacific, known as the "Puddle Jump," we had mixed emotions. Naturally, we admired their courage for attempting one of sailing's greatest challenges, but we were selfishly disappointed that they wouldn't be accompanying us to the Sea of Cortez.

At thirty, Rick had quit a high-profile career to sail around the world with his fiancée, Holly, who'd been working at a marine hardware store primarily for the employee discount on boat parts. After a two-year refit and meticulous planning, they sailed No Worries out the Golden Gate and made an abrupt left turn.

Pushing hard for Puerto Vallarta, they were caught in a storm off Point Abreojos, the same place we got clobbered, that had them reconsidering their decision to go cruising. As cruel as the sea can be, after the weather clears and the magic returns, you eventually forgive and forget.

In addition to preparing for the 2,800-mile voyage from Mexico to the Marquesas Islands, the longest minimum distance between two points of land on earth, they had guests flying in from all over the U.S. for their wedding in a couple weeks.

The logistics of planning a wedding in a foreign destination dwarfed in comparison to preparing for a passage to the South Pacific. While both are monumental undertakings for a daring few, there's practically no support in the middle of the ocean if things go badly. With deadlines looming, they had no time to dally. Unless you've outfitted a boat to cross an ocean before, you'll never understand the amount of preparation it takes.

It was obvious that our ultra-laidback lifestyle was annoying to them; they struggled to stay focused as we begged them to join us at the bar again and again. We even had time to attend timeshare seminars. I'm not sure which I enjoyed more – the free zip-line tours or messing with the pushy salesman I had to deal with in order to get them. Our conversations usually went like this:

> *"If you buy a timeshare here, you'll always have a place in Puerto Vallarta."*
> *"Exactly my point. Why would I always want a place in Puerto Vallarta when I have a boat that can go anywhere, that I don't have to share, and can be anchored for free?"*

After being wed on the beach in Bucerias, just north of Paradise Village, Rick and Holly discussed taking on crew with some of their guests at the reception. Having more hands would allow the honeymooners to spend more time together. It can be a lonely month with just two people onboard because one person is always on watch while the other is sleeping.

Rick's brother-in-law, Brett, and Holly's best friend's husband, Tanner, jumped at the opportunity. So, just after the wedding, both men went home, quit their jobs, and booked one-way flights back to Mexico.

When Rick told me about taking on additional crew, I agreed that it was a good idea but expressed my concerns about taking untested crewmates on long voyages. Things can get ugly out there.

He wasn't concerned. "They're both cool guys, and we're happy to have the help."

A few weeks later, we'd grown tired of resort life and were back out cruising. Other than an incident when two drunk guys swam out to our boat, boarded us, and refused to leave, there was no negativity.

We were excited when No Worries anchored next to us in La Cruz. "Hey you guys, good to see you," Holly called from the foredeck. "We're here to make the final preparations for departure in a couple of days."

La Cruz is a good staging ground for departure because it's close to stores, has easy access to the ocean, and offers good protection from the prevailing northerlies. We met Brett and Tanner and watched them make numerous trips in the dinghy, ferrying in supplies for the month-long

☼ 🕴 ⊙

voyage. After everything was stowed, all No Worries needed now were favorable winds to carry her to the South Pacific.

We convinced them to meet us for a farewell game of beach bocce. Facing weeks at sea, they accepted the opportunity to put their toes in the sand one last time.

As we were playing, I offered Brett a beer from my cooler, "Por qué no?"

"¿Por qué no? Why not? That's kind of funny. You know, I'm thinking about opening a Mexican restaurant in the States. That might be a good name for one."

"¿Por qué no?" I responded.

> *Well, Brett went back home and started a successful chain*
> *of restaurants by that very name. I still contact him*
> *occasionally to remind him that he owes me free tacos for*
> *life in exchange for branding rights.*

Coincidentally, halfway through the first match, Rick saw their wedding photographer walking on the beach.

"Hey Eddie. What's going on, man? It's good to see you."

"You too, and congratulations once again. I'm here visiting my parents; they live over there," he said, pointing to a beach house on the water. "Come over and meet them; they love having guests."

A few minutes later, we were at the home of Pepe and Luisa Rodriguez. Pepe is a rancher and land developer, and Luisa is the daughter of one of Mexico's most prominent attorneys. They were not shy about their affluence. All of their children had attended Ivy League colleges and spoke perfect English.

We polished off numerous bottles of fine tequila, toasting good fortune to No Worries again and again.

Sipping it softly, Pepe would lick his lips, smile, and say, "¿Por qué no?"

The more inebriated he became, the more animated he was. He spoke about his ranchero in the highlands south of the city, one of the few

☼ 𝖙 ☉

remaining in the state of Jalisco, bemoaning the big cats that were slaughtering his livestock.

"Damn pumas," he grumbled, looking off in the distance.

At one point in the evening, he reached over, grabbed my arm, looked me fatherly in the eyes, and said, "If you get in any trouble in Mexico – any trouble at all – just tell them to call Pepe Rodriguez, and you won't be in trouble anymore."

On the dinghy ride back to our boats, with the stars reflecting on the water with such intensity that it felt like we were floating in space, the party felt far from over.

"How 'bout a final-final wind-down Por qué no aboard Marylee?" I suggested.

"¿Por qué no?" Rick answered on behalf of his crew.

To everyone's amusement, I belly-flopped into the water trying to board my boat. That stuff never gets old.

An hour later, I was down below strumming Cassidy – my acoustic Alvarez that was presented to me by Bobby Weir at my thirtieth birthday party.

> *I named it Cassidy after the riff from the song he played before handing it to me. I felt silly at the time for not even knowing a chord.*
>
> *The name has a connection to Bello Beach too. Although the song is written about Cassidy Law, the son of Bobby's friend who tragically passed away, it alludes to Neal Cassady, a Beatnik, and Merry Prankster. He and Ken Kesey, author of "One Flew Over The Cuckoo's Nest," were central figures at the 3rd Acid Test that happened on Bello in 1965. An unknown band played at the event, the Warlocks, that would later become "The Grateful Dead."*
>
> *Bobby is a good guy – super down to earth and friends with everyone. When I first met him at a house*

☼ ⚲ ☉

party at Rusty's, I had no idea who he was. Our
conversation went exactly like this:
   "So, Bob, what do you do for a living?"
   "I'm a musician; I play the guitar."
   People were giggling; I knew something was up…
   "You any good?" I kidded.
   "Not really, but it pays the bills."
   Our mutual friend Tommy O teased, "Yeah, I like
to tell folks, "My buddy plays in this little band…"
   I'll never forget the benefit concert Bobby, Phil,
and Stuball held for Tommy after he became terminally ill
with brain cancer. It was such a melancholy event, such a
soulful playlist, and such an outpouring of love.

Suddenly there was a commotion in the cockpit; I stopped
strumming to hear what was going on.
   "Stop picking on me! Why are you against me?" Tanner shouted.

We were all confused. Who was he talking to?

Rick tried to console him. "No one's against you, Tanner. What's
going on, man? Was it something I said?"
   Tanner stormed to the bow and sat by himself. He was upset and
didn't want to talk. That prompted us to end the party and kick the
scallywags off our boat.
   While having coffee in the cockpit the next morning, we spotted
Tanner sitting alone in the dinghy tethered to the transom of No Worries.
He was clearly in a floating doghouse of sorts, looking lonely, tired, and
dejected. Eventually Rick drove him to the beach, dropped him off, and
dinghied over to speak with us.
   "You guys aren't going to believe what happened last night. As
soon as we got back to our boat, Tanner and Brett started fighting. They
were really going at it too; we were afraid they were going to hurt each
other. We're not sure what to do now, but we can't have that on our boat."

☼ 🕈 ◉

Later that morning, we found Tanner sitting alone in a smoky cantina. He looked so far from home. A hazy recollection of the night before was replaying in his mind – a turn of events so awful it must have felt like a bad dream.

"I'm really sorry, you guys. I don't remember much about last night."

Sam put her arm around him and said, "It was a crazy night for all of us. Danny even fell overboard, do you remember that?"

"Vaguely. That's about all I remember. Oh, man, I'm probably getting kicked off the boat; they're meeting to discuss it right now."

Sure enough, after some deliberation, Tanner was asked to leave. It was a harsh, yet prudent decision based on the circumstances. The drama was so thick that Sam and I vowed not to talk about it.

The following morning, after Tanner loaded his luggage in the dinghy, they drove over so he could say goodbye.

"Nice meeting you guys, and best of luck on your adventure," he said over the idling outboard.

They buzzed away and landed on the beach. Tanner disembarked and disappeared behind a dilapidated palapa – off to catch his flight home that afternoon.

Coincidentally, about that time favorable winds filled in, beckoning the Puddle Jumpers to jump. The conditions everyone had been waiting for had finally arrived. One by one, they weighed anchor and bid farewell over the radio. Words of encouragement and blessings from friends filled the airwaves as their silhouettes disappeared over the horizon.

We expected No Worries to bid farewell at any moment. Instead, Rick dinghied over to speak with us. "This is really hard for me to say, but we're bailing on the South Pacific."

Although the last minute discovery of a leaky fuel tank was the lethal blow, the true issues lay in deeper waters. The emotional rollercoaster of arranging a wedding, recruiting a crew, and preparing the boat had taken its toll. Although they ended up cruising the Sea of Cortez, sadly, they never fully embraced it. To them, it was a consolation prize, far short of their goal of sailing around the world.

☼　⚐　⊙

When we bumped into them again in La Paz a few months later, we weren't surprised to hear that Rick had accepted a job back home and that they were putting No Worries up for sale. Disappointed, they put their cruising dreams on hold.

Years later, they bought a catamaran and are out cruising the Caribbean full-time, supporting themselves with books and videos. They found a way to live their dream after all. Rick and I remain friends; he's friends with Tanner, too, and he chalks the whole ordeal up to the idiocy of youth.

To me, it was a difficult reminder of the importance of crew compatibility, especially in the middle of the ocean. Every sailor goes a little insane after weeks of monotony and poor sleep. The crew you leave with and the crew you arrive with may vary greatly.

Chapter 19
Jurassic Park

Anchored off The Monas at Isla Isabella

We returned to a slip in Paradise Village to provision for our trip to the Sea of Cortez. After washing, waxing, watering, icing, charging, laundering, and refueling Marylee, we pushed her away from the dock. She shuddered against the resort's sinister tractor beam, mounted just above the pool bar, until she finally broke free from the coddled life.

By high noon, I was sailing naked on the high seas – an attempt to keep my clothes clean a little longer. We dropped the hook behind Isla La Peña, a massive Gibraltar-shaped rock covered with palm trees, cacti, and white bird guano. It was a delightful place to watch the sunset and sip sundowners.

That evening, blessed with a favorable long-range forecast, we set out on a passage to Isla Isabella in the wee hours of the night. By daybreak, after a sweet night of sailing, Isabella's peak loomed on the hazy horizon.

☼ 🏃 ☉

The conditions were much more favorable than on our previous attempt. As we looked for a place to anchor, we were mindful that Isabella's anchorages are "anchor eaters," so we were careful where we set ours.

The concern is that the anchor chain will wrap around the massive underwater boulders as the boat moves around, making it impossible to retrieve in an emergency. This becomes especially dangerous in a storm because if you're unable to escape breaking waves, there's a good chance you'll either sink or be bashed on the rocks.

A wise precaution is to tie the bitter end of the chain to the inside of the boat with a piece of rope. That way, if an anchor gets fouled, you can cut the boat free from the inside. After conditions subside, you can usually recover the ground tackle. At Isabella, however, there are rusty anchors littering the seafloor, hopelessly wrapped and begrudgingly abandoned.

To our delight, there were no other boats in the prime anchorage under the turtle-shaped rocks known as the Monas. We vowed to stay as long as conditions and provisions allowed.

Anxious to get ashore, we hopped in the dinghy, cranked-up our ever-cranky outboard, nicknamed the Sea-Burro, and buzzed around the island to the fish camp on the south side. Sally Lightfoot crabs scurried across the rocks, like clusters of spiders, where we landed the dinghy.

Isabella feels Jurassic, with thousands of pterodactyl-shaped frigates circling overhead. In the springtime, the island becomes an avian nursery where birds of different feathers do, in fact, flock together. While the frigates build their nests in the safety of small trees, the gulls and blue-footed boobies foolishly build their nests on the ground – where they must be constantly defended from the sea-going iguanas crawling through the tall grass. While the gulls dive-bomb intruders with loud, intimidating screeches, the goofy blue-footed boobies just stand there and honk. Clumsy and cross-eyed, with big blue feet, comedy appears to be their only defense.

☼   ⚓   ◉

After signing the registry at the naturalist center, documenting our visit, we spent the remainder of the day hiking around the extinct volcano with a lake in the caldera at the top.

As we dinghied up to Marylee, we could see the growth on her hull from being kept in jungle estuaries for too long. No wonder she felt so sluggish on the passage there. I spent the rest of the afternoon cleaning her bottom, surrounded by schools of tropical fish. When I came back aboard, bleeding and exhausted, I declared that our tiny boat was much too big.

After a peaceful week of perfect weather and picturesque diving, we were running low on everything except sunshine, fresh fish, and tequila – all of which were in great abundance. We were sad to leave such a fascinating place, but knew there'd be many more places like it in the Sea of Cortez.

So goes vagabond sailing… No matter how perfect a place is, eventually you are beckoned to move on. Together with our buddy boat, Dos Brisas, we set sail for Mazatlan one splendid afternoon.

Chapter 20
The Wicked Passage

"If anything is going to happen,
it's going to happen out there."
- Captain Ron

After a brief stop in Mazatlan, we departed for La Paz on a northwest tack with our buddy boat, Red Sky, to starboard. Marylee galloped along in a steady breeze. We were making good progress for the first couple of hours, until Red Sky lost momentum and began lagging behind.

"What's going on, Tony? Are you guys having trouble?" I radioed.

"Our bloody engine keeps overheating for some reason," he responded in a British accent. "I'm going below to get to the bottom of it. Stand by, Marylee; we'll hail you when we know more."

"They've probably sucked up a jellyfish or piece of seaweed into their engine's raw water strainer," Sam speculated. "That's the most common culprit."

"I certainly hope so; a heavy boat like Red Sky probably needs twenty knots of wind to keep up with us. On a long passage like this, there's plenty of time for the weather to change; I'd rather not straggle in these dicey waters."

"Well, at least the short-range forecast looks pretty good. It's supposed to stay under fifteen knots for the next forty-eight hours."

"Yeah, but remember how well we fared the last time we attempted La Paz?" "The only difference this time is that there's nowhere to run." "Even if everything goes smoothly, it's still a three-day passage across the Sea."

The radio chirped back to life…

☼   ☥   ☉

"Bad news, Marylee, we've got a blown heat exchanger and need to return to Mazatlan to get it fixed."

"That's a shame, Tony, but we'll have some top-shelf margaritas waiting for you in La Paz. Hopefully, we'll see you soon. Over."

"Thanks, Marylee; we're hoping it's a quick fix. Be careful out there, you two; sorry for pooping out on you. Red Sky over and out."

They turned around and instantly disappeared over the horizon. Alone on the long voyage, we missed having a buddy boat to share information with – like weather observations, whale sightings, and navigation hazards. It also meant there'd be no one to chat with in the wee hours of the night.

Fortunately, the winds were fair and the seas remained flat. By the end of the second day, we were halfway to our destination, with just 150 nautical miles to go.

"Thar' she blows!" Sam cheered, pointing to a spout in the distance.

Suddenly, whales were everywhere – in such great numbers that I slowed the boat down for fear of hitting one. Sharks too, with their fins carving the waterline as they patrolled the floating kelp.

The Sea of Cortez is an extraordinary place – the only tropical body of water that's technically not in the tropics. It teems with life in such abundance that Jacques Cousteau coined it "The Aquarium of the World," and Ed Ricketts described it as "ferocious with life" during his expedition with John Steinbeck – my favorite author and literary mentor. It's a special kind of beauty in the middle of the sea, where the teal water against the clear blue sky overwhelms the senses.

The wind built in the late afternoon and began gusting unfavorably on our nose. We adjusted our course in the building seas to cross the waves at a less bumpy angle and hardened the sails to reduce roll – the underlying cause for seasickness. If you're prone to it, you'll fare much better on a sailing vessel than on a powerboat due to the increased stability. To achieve a similar hardening effect, powerboats are often outfitted with sophisticated equipment or even small sails to stabilize them in sloppy seas.

☼ ☀ ☉

"I'm concerned about going up the Cerralvo Channel. If it's blowing hard out here, it'll probably be Force-10 in there. We can avoid it altogether by going over the north side of Isla Cerralvo. Although it's a longer trip, it'll probably be more comfortable than bashing up a confined channel. "What do you think?"

"I completely agree. According to the cruising guide, the Cerralvo channel is one of the most treacherous bodies of water in Mexico because the wind is funneled between the island and shore. Apparently, the San Lorenzo Channel is another nasty spot just beyond that. We can avoid both of them by going over Isla Partida too."

Isla Cerralvo's four thousand-foot profile loomed on the cloudless horizon – like a black monolith. It was nice to see land again, even if it was so very far away. As the wind speed and wave height increased, we put on our foulies and prepared for a long, wet night.

"Something tells me we're in for a blow. Let's batten down the hatches and get everything stowed before it gets any darker. And let's triple reef that mainsail."

The wind speed increased to thirty knots...

Marylee was bucking like a bronco through the darkness, flying off the tops of waves, and falling through the troughs – kicking up spray as she landed. As conditions worsened, we were barely making headway. Without much forward progress, I was ready to heave to.

After days of silence, the radio chirped to life...

"Sea Wings, Sea Wings, Sea Wings, this is Ladera Star," a voice sputtered.

"Ladera Star, Ladera Star, Ladera Star, this is Marylee," I interrupted.

"Marylee, this is Ladera Star, go ahead," the voice crackled.

☼ ⚚ ◉

"Sorry to step on your transmission, but we're twenty miles northeast of Isla Cerralvo and getting pounded out here. Just wondering if you have any weather updates."

"Affirmative Marylee – and it's not pretty. The wind is supposed to increase overnight to forty knots with gusts to fifty. Better run for cover if you can. Over."

"That's not what we were hoping to hear. What's your position? You're coming in loud and clear, so you must be close; over."

"We're ducking the storm behind Isla Cerralvo with another boat named Sea Wings. It's too deep to anchor here, but it's surprisingly calm behind this big rock. We're not leaving until conditions improve."

"Calm conditions sound pretty good right now; mind if we join you?"

"Affirmative, Marylee, we'll keep a light on for you. Ladera Star out."

Still several hours away, assuming we could make any headway at all, we pushed Marylee through the angry sea. The merciless waves slapped her bow sideways again and again.

"You need to get some sleep, Sammi. I'll take this shift and wake you in four hours. Don't worry, I'll be fine out here."

She begrudgingly went below and fell asleep. Alone in the cockpit, in my bright yellow foulies, I was drenched and cold. I tried to think of warm things – like a roaring fireplace at Christmas.

Hours went by. Struggling to see through the drenched binoculars, I scanned the base of the giant rock for the two boats every fifteen minutes. Finally, through the spray, I spotted their running lights. About that time, there was a horrible wobble in the rigging that could be felt throughout the boat. I knew exactly what it was.

"Sam, wake up! The mast is unstable – and we may lose it! Grab the wire cutters in case we need to cut it away; it could hold us on our side and sink us! And get the life raft and ditch bag ready too, in case we need to abandon ship!"

It was the second time since San Diego that we were preparing for the worst. Evidently, the pounding waves had taken their toll on the rigging

✡ ⚡ ☉

– stretching the cables beyond their adjustable limits. Now the top of the mast was gyrating back and forth, making the entire boat vibrate. We dropped the sails and started the engine.

Sam surveyed the situation and hollered, "We're almost there; just a few more miles to go!"

"Thank goodness. Had this happened last night, we'd be in a lot more trouble."

As we approached the island, the wind speeds diminished until it became eerily calm. Although we couldn't anchor, we were happy to be in relative safety – and in the company of other boats.

"Fine weather we're having this evening," I kidded the other captains.

"Glad to see you safe and sound, Marylee. What's it like out there?"

"Snotty, Ladera Star, really snotty. Eight to ten foot square waves with forty knot winds."

I went on deck to inspect the rigging, but was disheartened to find that it would require new parts to fix it. I temporarily stabilized the mast by lashing the halyards to various points on the boat and winching them down until everything was snug.

"Well, hopefully that will keep the stick up until we reach La Paz. I'm going below to get some rest. Goodnight."

"Okay, but what am I supposed to do now?" Sam asked, rubbing the sleep from her eyes.

"Maybe watch a DVD or read a book. Don't worry about steering unless we're going to hit something."

I killed the engine, and went below.

"Are you serious?" she protested. "Do you really expect me to just bob around out here all night?"

"Pretty much. There's no sense in running the engine, and we can't set sail with a compromised mast. Just keep an eye out and try not to hit anything."

I was awakened by the sunshine on my face, momentarily forgetting where I was.

"Good morning, Sleepyhead," Sam sang sweetly.

"Good morning. How was it last night? It doesn't look like we moved very much."

"It was fine, I guess, but I don't like just floating around. The lack of control was not relaxing at all."

The large whitecaps on the north end of the island were evidence that the storm was still raging. We estimated it was still blowing at least thirty. After several hours without any noticeable improvement, Ladera Star nudged her bow past the rocky point and into the churning whitewater.

"I'm going to stick my nose out and see how it looks."

Marylee and Sea Wings, a thirty-five foot trimaran, followed Ladera Star to sea. Once we got past the "island effect," where the wind and waves amplify as they wrap around the landmass, a favorable tide had us making decent headway through the sloppy seas.

"I feel better having other boats around us," I confided. "Last night was pretty terrifying, being alone on a stormy sea with a shaky mast."

"I know what you mean. There's definitely safety in numbers out here."

Side by side, the three boats pushed through the surging whitecaps. Marylee kept up with the larger boats through the chop, despite her nominal waterline – and my emergency jerry-rigging was holding the mast firmly in place.

Hours later, after chugging up the San Lorenzo Channel, we entered Bahia de La Paz. The moment we did, everything settled. It felt like paradise compared to the conditions we'd just endured. It felt like we were on vacation again.

We cracked Por qué no's, turned up the stereo, and danced around the sun-drenched foredeck. We were stoked to be in one of the most beautiful cruising grounds in the world. The best was yet to come.

☸ ⚲ ◉

Chapter 21
The Peace

Anchored at Ensenada Grande

L a Paz is one of Mexico's most exquisite gems. Situated at the end of a large, protected bay, it's an elegant city with a glamorous past. The wide tree-lined streets and palm-laden Malecón boardwalk are evidence of its former influence as a Spanish capital and naval stronghold. In more recent years, La Paz has been rated a top place to retire due to its casual lifestyle, dry climate, and accessible medical facilities.

Settled by a Spaniard, Sebastian Vizcaino, in 1596, La Paz became a haven for pirates and privateers – most notably Cromwell, who used the hidden harbor at Pichilingue as a staging ground to pounce on unprepared galleons passing by. He used the predictable evening winds to chase down and pummel his victims in the dead of night. Thusly, the Coromuel winds were loosely named after him.

Coromuels are katabatic winds that occur when the cool marine air from Baja's Pacific coast rushes over the low desert plains to the relatively warm waters of the Sea of Cortez. They are as reliable as clockwork,

✡ 🜚 ☉

blowing nightly from late spring through summer, extending far out to sea. With wind speeds that can exceed forty knots, they're a blessing to the residents of La Paz, who enjoy the natural air-conditioning most evenings, and a curse for mariners that aren't securely anchored in a protected cove.

Elefantes are similar nighttime winds but occur further north in the Sea of Cortez – around Bahia Los Angeles. They are highly predictable though – if you see cloud formations snaking their way down the mountainsides in the afternoon, resembling an elephant's trunk, you better run for cover before nightfall.

Fortunately, there are plenty of places to hide from the gusts around La Paz – none better than the happy isles of Espiritu Santo and Partida, just twenty miles north. Attached by a thin ribbon of sand, the two islands are the most visited in the Sea of Cortez. On the westernmost shore, there are dozens of protected white sand coves that seem as if they were purposely designed for boaters.

After repairing Marylee's rigging, taking care of personal matters, and provisioning, we headed out to explore the islands. As we approached the red rock shores speckled with cacti, we were surprised to see so many colorful wildflowers clinging to the cliffs. The desert was in full bloom.

Especially after a rainy hurricane season, like the previous year, springtime in Baja can be breathtaking. As the days lengthen and the weather and water gradually warm from south to north, cruisers meander up the Sea until they practically reach Arizona.

"Now this is what I expected the Sea of Cortez to be like," Sam said as she sunbathed on the foredeck. "No weather, no people, no worries."

I handed her a margarita and replied, "Can you believe we're finally here? This, my dear, is top living. We're at the right place at the right time, that's for sure. Cheers, Rabbit Ears."

"It's funny; I've heard so many other cruisers talk about how beautiful this area is, but words don't do it justice. Life is so easy here, it feels more like a houseboat trip on Lake Powell than an adventure on the sea."

☼ ⚓ ◉

"Just think of all the reefs we'll dive, mountains we'll climb, and beach bocce we'll play before we put Marylee on the hard in San Carlos."

The water was so clear we could watch our anchor fall to the bottom and set in the fine white sand of Ensenada Grande, our favorite anchorage there. The towering red rock formations that rim the steep canyons provide unequaled protection from the Coromuels. There's a white wooden crucifix on the cliff that acts like a sundial on the cove below. After a few days there, you're able to tell time by the position of its shadow on the water.

While modern cruisers covet snug anchorages like this, sailing vessels of yesteryear rarely ventured into these tight coves for fear of being bashed on the rocks if it suddenly became a lee shore. Without an engine, they were forced to anchor in exposed roadstead anchorages with plenty of room to escape.

Several wonderful days went by. Sam and I lounged on floatie-rafts until our tans turned two shades darker. The nights were calm and quiet. Except for an occasionally lapping wave, jumping fish, or the call of a seabird, there was utter silence.

Chapter 22
Jeep

As the end of the spring semester approached, Sam needed to return home to complete her dissertation at her university. A dedicated student, she spent most of her free time studying.

"After you return, we'll start the big push north," I said. "It's going to be amazing."

Despite our proven compatibility in confined spaces, the notion of having the entire boat to myself seemed opulent at the time.

Since Sam was flying out of Los Cabos, I decided to rent a car and drive her there. We left early in the morning so we'd have plenty of time to explore Todos Santos, an eclectic art colony, along the way.

Comprised of cafés and galleries, Todos Santos is a bright and cheery place – where savvy tourists find tasteful souvenirs. It's an oasis of palms and cacti on the cooler Pacific side of Baja, best known for Hotel California – immortalized in the Eagles' song of the same name.

Just south of town, the rolling highway parallels the pristine Pacific, offering quick glimpses of secluded beaches between the golden ravines.

"It's hard to believe that we sailed past this point six months ago," I sighed. "It seems like years have gone by. So much has happened since then."

"I know what you mean – time moves slower at sea. Every day is so unique. I guess that's why they're so memorable. I wish I didn't have to go; please promise you'll be safe while I'm gone."

"I will, Sammi; don't worry about me. If you have time, drive by the house and check it out if you can."

"Absolutely, I was planning to. Is everything alright with the renters?"

"Well, the rent on the house is being paid, but Gamora is late on the car payment, and isn't responding to my emails."

☸ 🧍 ☉

Sam and I kissed goodbye in front of the departure terminal. Even though she was only going to be gone for a couple of weeks, it felt strange to be alone. Although I generally enjoy traveling by myself, cruising is so much better when there's someone to share it with – so I invited some friends to visit.

On the drive back to La Paz, I looked for a beach I'd visited several years before. At km 68, I veered off the highway onto a dusty dirt road leading down to the beach. It meandered down a ravine until it reached a sandy wash that was too deep to continue without four-wheel drive. I parked next to the only other car there and started walking through the coarse, yellow sand.

The beach was immense yet intimate, with crumbling bluffs cradling it on either side. In the distance, I saw someone walking toward me – no doubt the driver of the other car. He was a gringo with a gray beard wearing an Aloha shirt. After some pleasantries about the pristine setting, he introduced himself.

"My name's Jeep, you know, like the car."

"Nice to meet you, Jeep. Do you live around here?"

"Yeah, just up the road in Cerritos; been there for twenty years. The States are too crazy for this old hippie. I left the mountains of Idaho for the best waves in the world – and I'll never go back."

"It certainly seems crazy these days, but before too long, this place will probably be crazy too."

"Tell me about it, man. Cabo has already become a Southern California suburb. At some point, I'll grab my boards and head further on down the road. Say, when your girlfriend gets back, I'd be happy to take you guys on a surf safari. I've got plenty of boards, and you can even crash at my place if you'd like."

"Wow, that's a generous offer. We may take you up on that. If you're in La Paz over the next couple of weeks and want to go sailing, here's my boat card."

"Right on. I've got some business cards in my car. I'll leave one for you."

☼ ⚓ ⊛

When I returned to my rental car, I found his card under a wiper blade. On it was an image of Baja, an oil painting of a stormy sea, with just two words on the front: "Jeep, Artist," and an email address.

The next day, I emailed him about commissioning a painting to commemorate our trip. I sent him a picture of Marylee set against the unmistakable Monas at Isla Isabella. A year and a half later, I received the completed work in the mail, with a note: "Dan, I hope you like it. Only pay me if you do. Be well, Jeep."

To this day, the image evokes emotions. Although it only represents a fleeting moment in time, as long as it hangs on my wall, Marylee will always be anchored at Isla Isabella.

Chapter 23
The Return of Grouchy

With Sam away, my life in La Paz was hot and bothered. I'd go for a jog and work on the boat in the morning, go to the movies just to be in air conditioning most afternoons, and write in my journal in the evenings. I slept soundly, stretched out on the V-berth like an elephant seal on a sunny rock. There's no better place to slumber than on a bobbing boat in becalmed waters.

Despite the tranquility, a dark force in racing leathers was bombing down the Baja peninsula at over a hundred miles an hour. It took three determined days on a monstrous motorcycle for Grouchy to reach La Paz. Never to disappoint, even after a thousand dusty desert miles, his arrival was more obnoxious than anticipated.

Disregarding the "No Motorized Vehicles" signs, he raced his bike up and down the marina sidewalk, pulling wheelies, as pedestrians fled in terror and shopkeepers boarded up windows. After a couple of passes, he parked the beast at the end of the dock and started walking toward Marylee. As he neared, I braced myself for a tsunami of sarcasm.

"Yo' Fitzy! Nice boat, Skippy; I've taken bigger turds."

Punchy from the long drive, he shed his leathers, took some tequila shots, grabbed the bottle and shot glass, and went out to make new friends while I went to the marina bathroom. By the time I returned, he'd charmed his way aboard a large trawler named Francis Ray with free shots and one-liners. Sprawled out in a leather recliner in their main salon, I overheard him complaining about his accommodations.

"I'm just sayin', a man of my caliber should have friends with bigger boats."

With Slasher arriving the following week, I decided to take him and Grouchy to Ensenada Grande on separate trips. It would be easy and relaxing to stay close to La Paz, and there are plenty of things to do out there.

It took all day for us to reach the shimmering orange anchorage with nary a ripple upon it. We played bocce ball on the beach and barbecued the catch of the day in total isolation.

We awoke to dead calm conditions. The stillness made for the best water visibility I'd seen thus far, so we decided to snorkel Los Islotes – a rock one mile off Isla Partida's northwest tip that teems with sea lions.

The Sea-Burro pushed the dinghy along nicely. As a precaution, though, I brought a handheld radio, a satellite phone, and rowing oars in case the temperamental outboard failed in open water. We hugged the island's coastline as long as we could before heading out to sea. The Sea-Burro was uncharacteristically cooperative and took us there without dying once. We tied up a mooring ball and jumped into the water with dozens of sea lions circling us.

They zoomed around, investigating us as we swam through the colony. When the smaller females began approaching us, the large bulls intercepted; jealously separating us. They became increasingly hostile to our presence, swimming in tight circles around us and blowing bubbles as if they were barking. Sensing danger, we made our way back to the dinghy and pulled ourselves aboard. Grouchy ripped off his mask.

"What the heck was that all about? It must be mating season," he griped.

"Don't know, but we're lucky we didn't get bitten. Did you see the size of their teeth?"

"Damn straight I did; those suckers could cause some serious damage. You know, sea creatures are often named after the land animals they most closely represent. Those things are called sea lions because they act like lions."

"What a bummer, the diving conditions are amazing out here. Hey, do you want to try snorkeling around that rock instead?"

Grouchy surveyed the rock I'd pointed to with binoculars and replied, "Yeah, that one looks okay; there's only one sea lion on top of it."

☼ ⚹ ☉

We anchored the dinghy in the shallows and dove in. After snorkeling halfway around the rock, the sea lion sat up and started barking at us. We gave him a wide berth, staying as far offshore as possible and trying not to be threatening.

To our dismay, the large bull charged down the rock, jumped into the water, and started chasing after us. I was horrified to see it behind us – blowing bubbles and looking mad as hell!

I outswam Grouchy back to the dinghy and clambered aboard. The sea lion was right on his flippers. He managed to scramble in the dinghy without getting bitten, but it was close.

"Holy shit, that thing almost got me! Guess those bachelors are banished from the colonies for good reason."

"Yeah, that thing is as mean as a junkyard dog."

"Oh, and thanks for swimming ahead of me – and leaving me to get eaten. Some kind of friend you are."

"It's like the time we were on the photo-safari in Africa, Grouch. You don't have to be the fastest Wildebeest to survive – you just can't be the slowest."

Chapter 24
The Pristine Stretch

Under sail near Puerto Los Gatos

Marylee was ready for an immediate departure when Sam returned.

"All I could think about was getting back to you and the boat. It was nice to see friends and family, but do you know how lucky we are?"

"I think about it everyday, constantly aware that we're living a dream. It wasn't the same without you, though; now the adventure can continue. So how was your trip? Everything okay back home?"

"The trip was good; everything went well, and the house looks okay. I didn't see any neighbors, but other than an overgrown garden, everything looks the same."

"That's good to hear," I said as I sifted through the mail she'd brought back. "I'm concerned about the car, though. Gamora still hasn't paid rent – and here's a $300 ticket for parking in a handicapped space."

That evening I terminated the car lease and arranged to have my cousin Lou pick it up the following day. The next morning, Violet sent me an apologetic email saying that she was glad that I was repossessing the car because Gamora had become "flaky and irresponsible."

We pushed away from the dock and began the trip northward. Just beyond La Paz, the Sierra de las Gigantas Mountains rise up. These 3000-foot orange and red striped monoliths separate the Sea of Cortez from the Pacific – and shield it from the Coromuel winds. The nights beneath them are still and quiet, with only the occasional call of a seabird across the inky calmness. Absent of pollution and population, much of this pristine stretch is a marine sanctuary – including an archipelago nicknamed "The Bay Area" because the islands share the same names as the California cities: Islas San Francisco, San Jose, and Santa Cruz.

The crescent-shaped sandy hook off Isla San Francisco, technically Isla San Francisquito, is as iconic to the Sea of Cortez as the Eiffel Tower is to Paris. It's as beautiful and protected an anchorage as any sailor could ask for. We hiked to the top of the green rock cliffs, strewn with minerals and gems, to take the obligatory picture of Marylee in that one particular harbor.

The following day, we tucked up tightly in Punta Evaristo on the Baja Peninsula. There we spent several perfect days atop floatie-rafts lashed to Marylee's stern.

One afternoon, a ponga rounded the rocky point and headed for us at a high rate of speed. Wobbling sporadically, lacking control, it bore down on us with no signs of stopping. Worried that the driver wouldn't see us on the floatie-rafts, we scrambled back aboard the boat.

At the last moment, he jammed his outboard into reverse and came to an abrupt stop a few inches from Marylee. I could smell booze on him from ten feet away.

"¿Langosta?" the hairy beast inquired.

"¿Por qué no?" Sam responded, slightly breaching usage etiquette.

After some price haggling, he promised to return with "dos gigantas en dos horas."

"You have two cervezas for me, señor?" he said with puppy-dog eyes, coveting the beer I was holding.

"My precious," I hissed, hiding it from his meddling eyes.

☼　⚐　☉

It goes without saying that a frosty-cold Por qué no is a valuable commodity in a parched desert – and this fiend was moving in on my supply.

If only he just wanted money…

"Here you go," Sam said, handing him two.

He sucked one down, cracked the second, and roared off.

"Now I can't wait for dinner," Sam said as she cannonballed off the bow pulpit into the clear water.

"We should butterfly them in butter and garlic – like the ones we had at the Santa Maria beach party."

"Yum. Those were the best," she said, climbing up the swim ladder, "and we've got fresh tortillas, avocados, and salsa to go with them."

That afternoon we decided to go sand skiing down the 200-foot dunes that backs the beach. After a grueling ascent, we eventually made it to the top. From that vantage point, we were looking down on Marylee resting in the golden cove below us. We began carving through the sand with big smiles on our faces – hopping back and forth down the hillside as if we were skiing moguls. It entertained us for hours.

Shortly after returning to Marylee, the dilapidated ponga reemerged and sped for us again.

"Here comes dinner!" Sam cheered.

Lacking every form of judgment, not to mention fashion sense, the inebriated driver waited too long to jam his engine in reverse and awkwardly rammed into Marylee despite my efforts to fend him off. He either didn't notice or didn't care about the chip he put in Marylee's gel coat – he just reached into an ice chest, held up two lobsters, and grinned.

"Dos gigantas."

I paid him, partially because it meant he'd go away, but dreaded what came next.

☼ 🕴 ◉

"You have dos mas cervezas for me, señor?"

I growled as he motored away, "Those were my last cold Por qué no's, and we're almost out of ice. From now on, I'm catching my own lobster."

"Quit whining about your stupid beer, you big baby. We'll find more ice along the way. Until then, you'll just have to drink it warm."

Although her words were clearly mutinous, the lobster actually went well with lukewarm beer.

Chapter 25
The Ice Run

The next day we sailed a few miles north to Puerto Los Gatos. It's a primitive setting consisting of a fish camp on the beach with some modest dwellings strewn about the hillsides. In need of ice to prevent our food from spoiling, we jumped into the dinghy to find some. The cantankerous Sea-Burro spit, sputtered, ran like a champ for twenty seconds, then died and refused to restart.

"Ornery bastard," I grumbled as I rowed in. "I'd swear this two-stroke is bipolar."

"That's funny," Sam laughed, "but in my opinion, it's just lazy."

We made a soft landing on the coarse sand beach in front of a thatched structure – where a group of men were huddled in the shade, dodging the merciless sun.

They mobilized quickly to greet us. Bringing a beautiful blonde to the remote coves of Mexico is a guaranteed way to meet the locals.

"Buenas dias, señor, ¿dónde puedo comprar un poco de hielo?" I asked the friendliest looking one.

"Adonde," he replied, pointing high on the hill to the largest home.

Sam started marching up the rutted dirt road with potholes large enough to swallow a small car and said, "Guess we're in for a hike."

Although the home looked finished from the beach, it was quite simple up close. The plywood front door stood wide open – revealing the family sitting inside. They peered out at us like bears in a cave. After an awkward silence, they motioned for us to enter and sit in their windowless living room.

From the confused expressions on their faces, they had no idea why we were there. Lacking the language skills to tell our story with the appropriate eloquence, I pantomimed our great voyage, complete with sound effects, while Sam pointed to Marylee anchored in the distance. Since they didn't seem interested and certainly weren't impressed, I got right to the point:

☼ 🕈 ◉

"¿Hielo?" I inquired with blistering succinctness.

"Si, adonde," the patriarch replied, pointing back down to the fish camp we just hiked up from.

"Wait a minute, the guys down there told us you had the ice up here, but now you're telling us it's back down there?"

"Si, mucho hielo allí," then he rattled off a bunch of stuff in Spanish that I only pretended to understand.

Discouraged and deprived, we bid farewell and started walking back down the road.

"Gracias por nada, muchachos. I guess I'm not surprised; other than a few solar cells, there doesn't appear to be any electricity here. How would they even make and store ice without electricity?"

Sam was confused too: "I have no idea. So, why was he so adamant about there being ice at the fish camp?"

"Beats me, but it doesn't matter. If they had ice to sell, surely they would have sold it. It's probably a good thing they didn't have it at the house because it would probably have melted by the time we reached the boat anyway."

As we neared the beach, we overheard a pickup truck barreling down the hillside behind us, kicking up dust like a West Texan on a Friday afternoon.

"Hey, it's the guy from the house," Sam said as he passed by.

He skidded to a stop in front of the thatched structure, walked over to an enormous wooden cooler, unlocked the padlock, and opened it. Then he motioned for us to help ourselves and take as much as we needed.

"Ah, now I get it," I said… finally getting it.

Transporting the slippery blocks across the scorching sand, however, proved to be both challenging and chilly. We struggled to clutch the cold, wet chunks as they melted away in the mighty sun. To the casual observer, we looked like dumbasses. One by one, we tossed the sandy, shriveled cubes into the dinghy until we had as much as our icebox could hold.

I handed the man forty pesos and thanked him, "Gracious, señor."

☼ 🏃 ◉

He handed me most of it back, smiled, and said, "De nada, mi amigo, de nada."

Chapter 26
The Perfect Anchorage

Tucked up tightly in Agua Verde

Cruising northward, we eventually reached ever-popular Agua Verde – a wide anchorage with high, colorful mountains that shield it from southerly winds. There's a small archipelago of rocks and reefs that block northerly swells too, so it's protected from most directions – a rare sense of security.

Marylee was anchored in a sheltered hook on the northwest side. The hike into town resembled a set from a western movie – complete with a tattered graveyard and tumbleweeds tumbling across the road. We moseyed down the cactus-lined street to the tiny tienda we'd read about in the cruising guides.

It was a hodgepodge hut built of plywood remnants with a corrugated metal roof. It leaned to one side, sagged in the middle, and had tarps for the doors. There were only a few dozen items on the dusty shelves, and the refrigerated goods were stored in a small ice chest near the check-out – making it feel more like raiding someone's picnic basket than shopping in a grocery store.

We emptied the shelves, buying as much as we could carry. We figured the more food and water we had, the longer we could stay away from civilization. The proprietor, Maria, tallied our total in her spiral notebook. Aside from her store, the only other place to buy food was a farmhouse that sold fresh goat cheese.

Since we expected the market to have grocery bags, we didn't bring any of our own – and Maria didn't have any either. We couldn't pass up the opportunity to buy provisions, though, because the store had limited hours and we were leaving the next day.

That forced us to carry the loose items in our arms. We comically kept dropping them in the dirt – then dropped more things in the dirt trying to recover the things we dropped in the dirt. Between the recent ice run and this shitshow, we learned to carry plastic grocery bags from then on.

We spent most late afternoons reading in Marylee's cockpit, watching the water boil with fish just before sundown. It's fun to watch cruisers come and go too. With a plethora of places to explore in these fine latitudes, they're driven to see what's around the next corner.

We spotted a black ketch approaching on the horizon. Once her sails were doused, she motored into our little cove and anchored right beside us. Puzzled why they anchored so close to us in such a large area; it seemed highly inconsiderate.

A few minutes later, a wind shift caused the boats to reposition. Now Marylee's stern was just a few feet away from their bow.

"Captain, you're way too close!" I shouted. "How much rode do you have out?

"Around fifty feet," he said, jumping to his feet.

"Fifty feet? But you're in twenty feet of water. I've got a hundred and twenty-five out – so we'll probably bump in the night if we swing. You should either let out more rode or anchor further away."

"Sorry 'bout that; we're beginners. We'll move down a bit," he replied in a syrupy southern accent.

Later on, Sam and I rowed the dinghy over to apologize for the unneighborly introduction. The captain and his partner stood up to greet us as we approached.

"Good afternoon. Sorry for the confusion back there; it's only our third time anchoring."

"No worries; thanks for moving. It's good to get well situated before it gets dark. Did you just buy the boat or something?"

"Yes, Sir. We bought it in San Carlos two weeks ago and have been scared shitless ever since. Man, it's the real deal out here. We thought the Sea of Cortez would be easy sailing until we got the crap kicked out of us crossing over from the mainland. Needless to say, our first crossing was almost our last. I kept asking myself, "Why the hell am I in the middle of all this?""

"Sooner or later, every cruiser asks themselves that. It's all about exposure – if you're out there long enough, at some point you're gonna wish you weren't."

It was remarkable that a couple from Oklahoma with no sailing experience would just buy a boat and head out to sea. Months later, we bumped into them in San Carlos. Their boat was immaculate, and they looked tan, fit, and remarkably younger than we'd remembered. Experience builds confidence, and they had no regrets about their decision once they overcame their fears. Every newbie cruiser must "learn the ropes," an idiom derived from the days of tall-masted ships.

We set sail for Puerto Escondido the next morning, mainly because we were desperately low on water. There's a fuel dock there with a water hose that would make filling our two 20 gallon tanks much easier than ferrying 5-gallon jugs by dinghy – especially since the sinister Sea-Burro was refusing to run.

The smell of brewing coffee wafted through the cockpit. The warm, dry air, calm conditions, and unlimited visibility gave the day a sense of endless possibilities.

Sam looked up from the cruising guide with a dab of white sunscreen on the tip of her nose and said, "It says here there's a sweet anchorage just ahead – with only enough room for one boat."

☼   ⚓   ◉

I located it on the chart and replied, "Yeah, it does look pretty nice – let's check it out. If no one else is in there, maybe we can stay for the night."

From a distance, we had trouble seeing the obscured entrance.

"It's supposed to be right there, but all I can see is solid rock."

As we got closer, the rock formations opened up to reveal a picturesque cove of unbridled perfection. We loitered in the private sanctuary for five straight days – drinking rationed water and living off the sea. Thankfully, we had plenty of beer cooling on the seafloor – in a mesh bag tied to a rope.

I spent mornings and afternoons spearfishing for our meals around the large rock outcroppings. Before I left San Diego, I'd purchased a plastic fish identification card that I zip-tied to my spear gun. I marked each fish on it with an edibility rating. As I became more familiar with the local marine life, I learned to pass on four-star fish and concentrate on hunting five-star ones.

"I can't believe this place," Sam sighed. "This is by far my favorite anchorage."

I concurred. Of the dozens of coves we'd been gunkholed in, this one seemed particularly poignant. Perhaps the defining point of our journey – the place where all hardships, fears, sacrifices, and costs dissipate into a sense of self-actualization.

> *I stayed awake that night thinking about how lucky I was to be there, counting all my blessings in life. There was a sudden sense of enlightenment – there is no other way to describe it.*

☼ ⚓ ☉

Chapter 27
Honeycomb Cove

Temporarily tied to the rickety dock in Puerto Escondido, we were psyched to have Marylee's water and fuel tanks filled. We hosed down the boat and ourselves with the cool freshwater; the accumulated salt deposits melted away upon contact.

Puerto Escondido is a natural treasure. Translated, it means "Hidden Port" – a fitting name for its remarkable snugness. Encircled by hills and high mountains, with only a thin ribbon of water connecting it to the sea, it's one of the best "hurricane holes" in Mexico because it's protected from all sides. It isn't clean and pristine, like the other anchorages around it, but it is the most protected. Cluttered with dilapidated boats and equally dilapidated people, it wasn't a place we wanted to stay long.

After motoring past "the waiting room," a nook at the entrance of the harbor where deep-draft vessels wait for high tide to cross the shallow bar, we set a course to Honeymoon Cove on Isla Danzante – one of the finest anchorages in the Sea of Cortez.

We arrived in the early afternoon and struck out to explore the island we'd heard so much about. That evening, as I was barbecuing fish on the grill, Sam was making beer bread in the galley.

"There sure are a lot of bees down here."

"There's a bunch out here too; hopefully they'll buzz off at sundown."

Due to the lack of fresh water on the barren rock islands, coupled with an unusually large hatch from a wet hurricane season, cruisers were under constant threat of being swarmed that spring. Once thirsty bees smell fresh water, they will aggressively seek it out. The bees in Baja are a dangerous Africanized hybrid variety, too, that will attack with little provocation.

The bees became even more bothersome the following morning. Shooing them from her face, Sam went below to get some relief but found

☼ 🜨 ◉

none. They were just as numerous in the cabin. She instinctively swatted the one crawling up her arm and killed it.

The hum of the swarm immediately intensified in both pitch and volume. Now it sounded dangerous.

"Ouch! I just got stung. We've got to get out of here!"

"Ouch! Me too – let's go, let's go, let's go!"

I bolted to the foredeck and started weighing anchor. Although there weren't many bees on the bow, the cockpit was canopied in a black cloud of them. As I was hauling the chain up, I felt one crawling up my neck. With both hands occupied, all I could do was grunt as it stung me.

At the helm, cleverly wrapped in a blanket, Sam piloted us out of the cove and into the channel. Within a couple minutes, there were only a few stragglers left.

"Honeymoon Cove? They should have called it Honeycomb Cove."

Sam laughed, "Yeah, its probably not the best place to begin a marriage – especially if your spouse is allergic to bees."

We set a course for nearby Loreto. After weeks in the wilderness, we looked forward to the sweet taste of civilization.

Sam was stoked. "I'm excited to get ice cream and fresh vegetables. I've been craving a green salad for weeks."

"I'm looking forward to a hot shower, clean laundry, and someone else to catch and cook our dinner. Tell you what, let's go out to a nice restaurant here to celebrate."

A byproduct of living a primitive lifestyle is a much greater appreciation for simple luxuries. Sometimes returning from a long voyage can be as exhilarating as leaving on one.

☼   🚶   ☉

Chapter 28
Befriending a Wizard

In fair weather, the roadstead anchorage in Loreto can be quite pleasant, but lacking any protection from the open sea, skippers must keep a watchful eye out for deteriorating conditions. The reward of being anchored so close to town is worth the risk, though, and there's usually a steady sea breeze that keeps it cool and insect free.

We dropped our hook next to a Vagabond 47 ketch bowing gently in the rolling swell. More pirate ship than pleasure craft, Mija invokes tall ship nostalgia in all who admire her. Her regal transom windows, soaring bowsprit, and spacious working deck give her a ruggedly traditional appearance.

"Whoever they are, they sure mean business," I said as we dinghied past. "Just look at the size of that ground tackle."

Perhaps sensing our presence, a wizard materialized on deck. I didn't see a puff of smoke, but there probably was one. His flowing white beard and glacier blue eyes were piercing from a distance.

"Ahoy there."

"Hola, señor. We were just admiring your beautiful boat. It's very impressive," Sam called back.

"Muchas gracias, yo soy Erik. Come aboard and check it out if you'd like."

We took him up on his offer. I love seeing other boats and rarely pass on the opportunity to board one. After climbing the stout swim ladder, we introduced ourselves and shook his callused hand. He was clearly an old salt.

"Terry, this is Sam and Dan," he said as his partner joined us in the cockpit, "they're from that sweet Nor'Sea 27 that just pulled in."

"Nice to meet you guys. Can I get you something to drink?"

"¿Por qué no?"

☼   🕴   ◉

After a few rounds, they gave us a boat tour. Mija was even more beautiful below deck than she was above. It felt like a solid piece of furniture, updated and airy – and impeccably well maintained.

Back in the cockpit, we swapped stories and shared local knowledge. Together with Quinn, their effervescent gray Terrier, they'd been cruising Mexico for the better part of a decade. It was profoundly apparent that they were masters of the sea.

"So where are you guys headed?" Sam asked.

"Up to Bahia Conception, then we'll cross over to San Carlos in mid-June," Terry replied. "We usually take the boat out of the water there to avoid the summer heat and dodge hurricane season."

"That's great to hear – because we're headed to the same place and doing the same thing. Hopefully we'll see each other along the way."

"No doubt we will," Terry replied, "but we're leaving tonight to have dinner on a friend's boat anchored at Isla Coronados."

"Isn't it too late to sail over there this afternoon? It's over twelve miles around the island."

"Not if you take the shortcut through the reef," Erik said cunningly, "then it's only three."

"That passage is not advised," Sam warned. "According to the cruising guide, that channel is really narrow and dangerous. It recommends going around the island unless you have a shallow draft vessel – and even then, it sounds pretty sketchy."

"Well, we've been through it many times without any problems," Terry said reassuringly, "and we draw six feet. It only takes thirty minutes, and it's beautiful sailing through all that colorful coral."

"Good to know; maybe we'll try it in the morning," I said as I stood up to leave.

"Hold on a second. We've got something for you guys." Terry ducked below and reemerged a minute later with an envelope that she handed to Sam. There was a gift certificate inside that read:

"Breakfast for 2 at Marco's Restaurant."

☼ ⚕ ☉

"We won it as a raffle prize at the Loretofest Sailing Rally last month. Since we won't be back here for awhile, you guys should use it."

"Thanks," Sam replied, "we're looking forward to a big breakfast – and a free one sounds even better."

The next morning, after taking a two-dollar shower at a one-story hotel, we found Marco's restaurant and presented our coupons. Marco, the portly proprietor, welcomed us like long-lost relatives and sat us at a table on a terrace surrounded by pink bougainvillea.

"Do you like biscuits and gravy?"

Sam giggled, "That's a silly question, Buster; everyone likes biscuits and gravy."

"Tell you what… I'm going to bring you the best biscuits and gravy in all of Baja."

"Sounds great. We haven't seen that on a menu anywhere else in Mexico. We'll take two."

"Muy bien," Marco sang as he danced his way back to the kitchen. "Muy bien."

"Good choice Sammi; it sounds like it's the house specialty. He sure seems excited to make it for us anyway."

One minute and fifteen seconds later, Marco returned with two steaming plates of mushy mounds that he proudly placed in front of us. He lingered around to watch our reaction to his epicurean masterpiece.

Sam took a bite. From the look on her face, something was terribly wrong. Her eyes rolled back in her head, and she stretched her neck to swallow it without chewing – like a pelican gulping down a fish.

"Yummy!" she said unconvincingly.

It was my turn. There was no escape.
His beady eyes were on me…

I took a small bite. The initial sour flavor gave way to the taste of rancid meat. Fighting off my gag reflex, I pushed it down and gave Marco a thumbs-up.

"¡Muy Bien!" Marco cheered. "It's my first time making it. My American customers are always asking me for biscuits and gravy, so I decided to give it a try."

Once he disappeared into the kitchen, we pushed the plates aside, left the coupons and a tip, and dashed for the door. Whatever was on that plate – and we both had our own theories – we refused to ingest any more of it.

Shortly thereafter, we found a taco stand with amazing shrimp tacos that took the lingering taste out of our mouths. We spent the remainder of the day exploring the charming town and gathering provisions.

The historic Mission Loreto in the center square was the first in a chain of California Missions, spaced "one day by horse" apart up the El Camino Real trail. The stone courtyards are encircled by cactus gardens that were originally planted to fortify the perimeter from intruders.

That evening, we enjoyed a candlelight dinner on the terrace of a fine restaurant. There, we discussed our upcoming bike ride across Europe.

"Of course it will be incredible, but I'm already missing Marylee," I said with some reservations. "Why would we ever want to leave this lifestyle?"

"Seasons change, Sweetheart – and everyone says that the summers are unbearably hot here. Besides, Europe will be a nice change of pace. We'll be cycling across beautiful countries and exploring new places. Can you imagine how fit we'll be after riding every day all summer?"

"You're right. It's going to be amazing. It's just hard to think about downsizing from a twenty-seven foot boat to living in a tent. It will be a big downgrade in accommodations, but at least we won't have to worry about storms. Cycling should be relatively stress-free."

"Speaking of accommodations, have you heard from Violet lately? Is she going to extend the lease?"

"Haven't heard anything, but she's paying rent on time. Hopefully she'll want to stay; I'd rather not be hassled with renting it again."

"Yeah, that would probably be best – especially if they're taking care of the place. If they extend it for another six months, maybe we can return in the autumn and spend another winter in the tropics."

"Hearing you say that makes me feel better about leaving. Walking away from this lifestyle makes me wonder if we'll ever recapture it again."

Chapter 29
The Prison Reef

With restocked provisions and full bellies, we set sail for Isla Coronados the next morning to catch up with our friends on Mija. Like a tight band of musicians, Sam and I seldom needed to speak when maneuvering the boat. We knew Marylee so well that operating her had become second nature to us.

We decided to follow Mija's advice and take the shortcut through the coral reef to the anchorage on the other side. In a radio conversation with them just before we departed, they told us they saw no less than twelve feet of depth the night before. Certainly, if that big pirate ship made it through safely, so could little Marylee.

The calm seas, clear water, and bright morning sun provided optimum viewing conditions of the coral bottom. The water was so clear that it was unnerving because everything on the seafloor looked so close. Unfortunately, the charts of the area were inaccurate – a prominent reason the shortcut was discouraged in cruising guides. With visual navigation being the best way to judge hazards on the bottom, Sam stood lookout on the bow as we pressed forward.

There were waves breaking on a brown ledge protruding from the surface directly in front of us. Fearful of being holed by a jagged reef, we typically go to great lengths to avoid them altogether. This time, however, we took a chance.

I piloted Marylee through twenty-feet of turquoise water with fanning vegetation on the seafloor. With a constant eye on the depth gauge, I called out the diminishing digits, knowing all too well that our fully laden boat would be aground at 4.2 feet.

"Eleven, ten, nine, eight," I called in a steady rhythm. "Sammi, does it look like it's getting any deeper in front of us?"

"I think so. Head ten degrees to port."

The depth gauge dropped to seven, then to six.

"We're almost aground!" I yelled. "Can you see the channel?"

"No, it all looks the same. It's shallow everywhere."

"Five feet. Hang on, Sammi, we've got to get out of here!"

I jammed Yanmar into full reverse in a futile attempt to back out of the hellhole we had entered. The tidal currents, moving swiftly across the shallows, caused Marylee to careen uncontrollably toward the ledge. Without steerage, impact seemed imminent. I rammed the throttle full speed ahead and regained control just in time to avoid a collision.

To our dismay, we somehow slipped over the reef and were now encircled by a jagged ring of coral.

"We're trapped – and there's not enough room to turn around! Do you see any way out in front of us?"

"It looks like there's a gap over there," she said, pointing to it. "Head toward that rock, then turn to starboard when I tell you to."

Trusting her judgment and visual perspective, I drove Marylee toward rocks that looked entirely too shallow for us to pass over.

"Hard to starboard, now!"

I turned just in time to see a coral head slip past our portside.

"4.7… 4.6… 4.5," I yelled. "Sammi, brace for impact!"

"Hard to port!" she screamed. "Hard to port, now!"

I slammed the helm over – and watched the depth gauge drop to 4.3. There we were…just an inch from disaster. We hovered there for what seemed like an eternity – until the gauge slowly began trending in our favor.

"4.4… 4.8… five feet – keep it up, Sammi, it's getting deeper."

A minute later, we were in fifteen feet of water and safely on the other side. We motored into the sandy bay and anchored next to Mija.

My voice quivered, "That was way too close."

Later on, after a few Por qué no's, we jumped into the dinghy and retraced our route through the jagged gauntlet. Although it wasn't clear how we managed to get inside the reef, the escape route was evident. I kicked myself. The thought of being shipwrecked just to save a few hours will forever haunt me. Thankfully, Marylee sailed away unscathed… Wish I could say the same for her captain's confidence.

☼ ⚓ ◉

Chapter 30
Schooled by Experts

O ver the next couple of weeks, with a sense of closure creeping in, we soaked up every moment of the cruising life. Adapting to the ever-warming climate, we hiked mountains in the cool morning, took siestas at midday, and spearfished for dinner in the late afternoon. Thankfully, the surrounding seawater kept Marylee relatively cool down below. Beamier boats with more interior volume were becoming oppressively hot as summer set in.

In San Juanico Cove, a picturesque bay scalloped by numerous beaches, Marylee was tucked up tightly between two giant rocks.

Sam read from a cruising guide, "They call that one Prudential Rock because it resembles Gibraltar. Hmm, that's interesting… Apparently all four beaches here are unique. That one is full of gems; that one has fossils in the cliffs; that one is good for shelling; and that one has the Cruiser's Shrine on it."

We'd been hearing about the Cruiser's Shrine since San Diego. It consists of a lonely little tree on a rocky beach, adorned with weathered ornaments left by thousands of cruisers. It's a tribute to every crew that reached this splendid part of the world. The ornaments are made from all matters of material: old tennis shoes, broken boat parts, and bikinis – hanging from every branch. Names and dates are scribbled on them to commemorate their respective voyages.

We affixed ours to a high branch. It was made from a blank CD with "Marylee '04" written across the top and "Sam and Dan" below. We looked proudly upon our contribution as it flashed brilliantly in the afternoon sun. After watering the little tree, as is customary for cruisers to do, we rowed back to Marylee.

The following morning, we overheard Terry on the radio hailing another boat. The signal was so clear that we knew they must be nearby.

Sam hailed them on the VHF: "Mija, Mija, Mija, this is Marylee."

"Hey Marylee, this is Mija."

"Hi Terry. You're coming in loud and clear. Where are you guys?"

"We're in Caleta Ramada, just north of San Juanico Cove. Come join us – this is one of our favorite anchorages."

We weighed anchor and made the short trip around the point.

"Mind if we check in to the Ramada?" Sam kidded as we drove past them.

"Hey you guys," Terry called back. "We were hoping you'd catch up with us. Isn't this place spectacular? Erik's been catching triggerfish off the point all day. He claims it's one of the best fishing spots in the Sea."

"Don't know about that, but the beach looks like prime bocce grounds to me. If you guys aren't too chicken, we challenge you to a match this afternoon."

"You're on. Let's meet by the big cactus around six."

"Cool. We'll bring the margaritas; you bring your wallets," Sam giggled.

"You guys are going down…"

Dinghy Bar

As it turns out, that particular strand will forever be known as the best beach bocce course in Baja. The undulating white sand fairways meander through the thorny green vegetation as if it was specifically designed for the purpose.

We mixed cocktails on the bow of our dinghy and ate fresh ceviche off the bow of theirs. Throughout the trip, our dinghy bow was transformed into a mobile beach bar – complete with little cocktail umbrellas I'd brought from home.

By the time we finished our championship match, which Sam and I heroically won, it was completely dark. As we were getting in our dinghies, we heard strange gnawing sounds coming from the opposite end of the cove.

"Did you hear that?" Erik asked.

"What the heck is that?" I replied. "It sounds like coyotes."

Terry chimed in, "When I was running Quinn over there this morning, there were dead squid all over the beach. Maybe coyotes are eating them?"

"Let's go check it out," Erik said with a twinkle in his eye.

"Alright," Sam agreed, "but let's not get too close. If it is a pack a coyotes, we should stay in deep water."

The closer we got, the more perplexed we became. The noise had a high pitch squeal and occasional honk. It definitely wasn't coyotes. I reached for my dive light and shined it on the beach...unsure of what we'd see.

The light exposed thousands of Humboldt Squid, the most aggressive creature in any ocean, darting out of the water and thrashing about on the beach. Equipped with 36,000 tiny teeth and one long razor-sharp beak, they're incredibly nasty creatures with a bite-force greater than a lion.

The local fishermen refer to them as "diablos rojo," or "red devils," because of their fearsome reputation for attacking anything that's unlucky enough to be in the water with them. Oddly enough, thousands of them were exterminating themselves – squirting a final stream of water into the air before honking hollowly on the beach.

"First person that gets squirted by one wins," I wagered just before getting squirted by one.

☼ ⚲ ◉

"What's causing them to do this?" Sam asked. "Is it normal for them to beach themselves at a certain time of the year?"

"Beats me," Erik responded. "Of all my years sailing in the Sea, I've never seen anything like this. They're certainly not mating or giving birth, it appears to be mass suicide."

Ranging in size from two to four feet, they began ramming our inflatable boats from every direction. Although it seemed funny at the time, we later understood the danger we were in. Had we ended up in the water with them, we would have been eviscerated in seconds.

Marine biologists are perplexed by this behavior. It's a maritime mystery. Theories suggest that they are either being chased by predators, disoriented from eating toxic algae, or instinctively trying to eradicate disease.

The foul odor of dead squid on the beach became more pungent with each passing day. Eventually, like in Chacala, the smell chased us away. After a bumpy sail up a geode-strewn shore, alongside Mija and a black ketch named Cool Change, we entered the protected waters of Conception Bay.

Conception Bay is a sea within the Sea. The warm, shallow water and picturesque anchorages offer something for everyone. Some of the coves are populated, while others are wilderness. There are even two restaurants there, Bertha's and Ray's, that we'd heard good things about. It's the type of place that you can stay for seasons because there's a lot to do – and the living is easy.

"Greetings, Marylee, welcome to Burro Beach," the radio chirped just after we anchored. "I'm Geary in the bungalow with the floating bar in front of it. Stop by for a cocktail when you come ashore."

"Now that's what I call hospitality; we'll take you up on that offer."

We rowed past his makeshift floating bar in four feet of water, admiring its simplicity. It consisted of a patio umbrella drilled into the sand with a floating tabletop around the pole.

☼ 🏃 ⊙

Geary's Floating Bar

Geary's thatched bungalow was equally endearing. There was a hammock on the front porch, tied between two driftwood posts. Atop it, there was a pair of aircraft earmuffs, a blanket, and a sign that read: "Siesta, do not disturb" that he hung while he napped.

He had a magnetic board near the front door to indicate his whereabouts. It read:

- In town
- At Bertha's
- Out fishing
- At the cantina
- Next door
- At Ray's
- Gone

I located the magnet and said, "Based on the board, he's at Bertha's. Wherever that is?"

Just then we spotted a man walking toward us on the beach. He wore dark sunglasses and had a rolled-up red bandana around his head.

"Howdy folks."

"You must be Geary. We're Sam and Dan off Marylee."

"Nice to meet you Sam and Dan off Marylee," he said with a smile. "I was admiring that beautiful little boat of yours. She's got some nice lines."

"And we were admiring that floating bar of yours," Sam replied. "What a great invention that is."

"Yeah, it's pretty popular around here. Come on inside and make yourself comfortable. Can I get you a drink? I'm told I make a damn good margarita."

"¿Por qué no?"

Although he wasn't a mariner, he was as connected to the cruising community as any boat in the anchorage.

"I'm heading into Mulegé tomorrow if you need me to pick you up anything," he offered as he handed us our drinks.

"Thanks, Geary, but we're planning to do a big shopping trip in the next couple of days. We're running low on everything."

"Wish I could offer you a ride, but my dune buggy only has two seats," he said, nodding at the purple one parked out front, "and I need one seat for my groceries."

"No worries, we'll find a way into town."

"So, Geary, how long have you lived here?" Sam asked.

"Been here almost seven years," he said between puffs of his Gordo cigar. "I used to be a supermarket executive but quit to find a better life. This place isn't for everyone, but I can't imagine any place I'd rather be. There's always nice people passing through, like you guys, so I'm either making new friends or surrounded by old ones."

"You're a boatless cruiser," Sam kidded.

"Ah yes, it's a beautiful life on the water, but it isn't for everyone. Certainly not for me."

We later learned of Geary's legendary benevolence in those parts. He had a reputation for extending a helping hand to anyone in need. We awoke the next morning, and every morning thereafter to him playing Amazing Grace on his bagpipe at sunrise. Shortly thereafter, he'd give a

⚓ ⚓ ☉

weather report over the radio, combining professional forecasts with his local interpretation of them.

We found living on Conception Bay to be pretty effortless – like living above a seafood market. Although there's an abundance of pintail scallops and delectable fish in the region, the most prized "fruta del mar" are the chocolate clams, or "chocolatas." Although they inhabit the same sand bars as the more prevalent butter clams, their mocha brown shells and distinct flavor are easy to distinguish.

We dined aboard Mija most nights, eating Erik's catch of the day. We jumped at the opportunity whenever they invited us because Terry is such an outstanding cook. She whipped up a variety of delicious dishes, including Thai fish stew, scallops in a mushroom cream sauce, and chocolate clam pizza.

We ate at Bertha's too. For a couple of dollars, the sweet but stern proprietor would make us whatever we wanted, whether it was on the menu or not. She'd even prepare the fish we caught that day.

After breakfast there one morning, I noticed a sign that read: "Showers" on the side of the building. I pointed to the sign, and asked Bertha if I could take one.

"Si," she responded, "cincuenta pesos, señor."

Excited by the prospect of a shower, especially since Marylee's water tanks ran dry a few days prior, I jumped at the opportunity. I grabbed my towel and shaving kit and followed her to a makeshift outdoor enclosure consisting of four posts, a privacy tarp, and a muddy piece of plywood for a floor. She filled up a five-gallon bucket from a water tank, handed me a soup ladle, and gestured that I ladle the water on my head.

There's nothing more refreshing than the simplicity of Mexico.

The following morning, we hitchhiked into the nearby town of Mulegé. Hitching a ride in Mexico is easy – any Mexican with a pickup truck headed in your direction will let you jump in the back. It's an

☼ ⚓ ☉

incredibly hospitable country, that way; culturally conscientious when it comes to sharing resources.

Mulegé is one of the most fascinating towns in all of Mexico. Built on a river and shaded by a thick canopy of date palms, it feels exotic – like a setting in Southeast Asia.

We spotted Geary's dune buggy parked in front of an open-air cantina on the main street and found him at the bar watching a soccer match.

"Hey Enrique," he said to the bartender, "can you believe these two youngsters are going to ride a tandem bike across Europe this summer?"

"Better them than me," Enrique responded.

"You've got that right," Geary chortled. "You see in Baja, it's all about conserving energy, not expending it."

We bought enough provisions for a final week in Conception Bay. Although getting the groceries back to the boat was a cumbersome task, it felt good when we were finished. Relaxed and tanned, without a care in the world, we spent the remaining days on floatie-rafts soaking up the rays.

The threat of hurricanes was becoming more evident with each passing day – as air and sea temperatures steadily climbed. Satellite imagery outlined tropical depressions beginning to develop off Acapulco and spin up the Pacific – indicative of the more powerful storms that would track north later in the season. That, plus the rising heat and humidity, had us ready to hightail it to the mainland and wrap up our cruise.

A few days later, we set sail for San Carlos at sunset, ninety-two nautical miles away. Unlike the epilogue, we weren't running for our lives on this pleasant passage across the Sea. As dawn lifted, the iconic Tetas de Cabra red-rock formations became visible from a distance. Similar to the arch in Cabo San Lucas, it was the symbolic finish line of a fantastic voyage. Surprisingly, other than the Slasher-broken head and rigging repairs in La Paz, we had no major mechanical issues during the three thousand mile cruise. Marylee proved to be as reliable as she was beautiful.

Sam and I embraced. We'd made it. We thanked Marylee, Yanmar, and Otto for a job well done, and cursed the Sea Burro for being such a bastard. I still had most of the money I'd left La Paz with – partly because we were living off the sea and partly because there weren't many places to spend it.

In preparation for storage, we washed and packed everything away as neatly as possible. We even "pickled" the engine with vinegar to remove the salt and put tin foil over the portholes to block the intense UV rays that would otherwise bleach the interior.

It was sad to see the stripped-down boat being hauled from the water and put into dry storage with hundreds of other boats. Regretfully, we closed her up, bid her farewell, and hopped on a bus bound for Phoenix…

Where a Category 5 shitstorm was about to make landfall.

☼ ⚲ ◉

Chapter 31
The Shocking News

A fter so many months in Mexico, we expected our homecoming to be a blessing and a curse – and oh, what a curse it would be. Away from Marylee, I already felt like a fish out of water.

After living a predominately hunter-gatherer lifestyle for so long, it was painful reacclimating to modern society. Our sense of freedom evaporated the further we got inland.

The Arizonan interstate felt smooth as glass compared to Mexico's Federal Highway 15. There was a sense of exhilaration to be back in our homeland, but the fast-paced lifestyle felt distinctively foreign. We made a pact to stay laid-back.

Our room at the airport hotel seemed palatial compared to our tiny boat. It had a TV with programs in English, unlimited hot water, and air conditioning. Excited about having internet access, I booted up my computer to check my email. Between messages from friends and family welcoming us home, there was an email from Violet terminating the lease agreement at the end of the month – and another from the Sheriff's Department that read:

> *"Mr. Fitz, Please contact Lt. Dixon immediately about the security of your property in Bello Beach."*

"What the heck?" I mumbled, nervously dialing the digits. It took three attempts to dial them correctly.

"Hi, Lieutenant Dixon, I'm Danny Fitz, calling with regard to the email you sent me. What is this all about?"

"Mr. Fitz, I'm a detective on the Sheriff's Vice Squad that's been investigating your property for several months now. Do you know who you rented your house to?"

"Yes, Violet Storm. I rented it out to her a few months ago."

"Do you know who she is – the family she's from?"

☼ 🏃 ◉

"Um…"

"Perhaps you've heard of some of her family members?"

He told me their names.

Indeed, I had – they were sultans of sexploitation. I'd even watched a recent movie about their scandalous rise and murderous demise, starring some of my favorite actors.

"Well, Mr. Fitz, we suspect your property has been turned into a brothel."

"You've got to be kidding me."

"Unfortunately not. We've had an undercover team staked out there for five months, following up on an online ad. You need to return home immediately; if the Feds get involved, you could lose your house."

Chills ran down my spine as the officer delivered the shocking news…

I felt weak in the knees – was I going to faint?

Surely this was a bad dream; surely it was some kind of joke…

Then it dawned on me…

Gamora's role in all this – and the fact that I rented my car to her!

Was I going to be implicated? Surely they ran her license plate when she parked there – showing the car registered to me. The more I thought about it, the more anxious I got. It looked bad. Would I be arrested when I returned – and go from self-actualizing in paradise to a jail cell in California?

☼ ⚘ ⊙

I stayed awake that night, tossing and turning. Oh, what a fool I'd been. In my haste to fulfill my dreams, I made the fatal mistake of not listening to a woman's intuition. Sam was right all along.

I kicked myself for accepting what was given to me – and not properly vetting their applications. Although I did verify employment, now I questioned everything. Suddenly so many things started making sense – like why rent was being paid with cash cards, and even Violet's quirky email address with ties to her famous family.

> *For years I wondered whether it was just a coincidence*
> *that the authorities notified me within hours of returning to*
> *the U.S. – until I learned about CLETS, California's*
> *telecommunications tracking system for suspects and*
> *people of interest. The cops were waiting for me to return.*

☼   ⚘   ⊙

Chapter 32
Taking it Back

Fortunately, I wasn't arrested when I returned home. Instead, the lieutenant was forthcoming with details of his investigation.

"There were two other properties involved in addition to yours. When a suspected John called the number on the online ad, they were instructed to go to a local convenience store at a specified time and wait for a call on the payphone there to get an available address."

Without enough hard evidence to make arrests, and with just one week away from his retirement, the lieutenant sought closure to his thus far fruitless investigation. Ironically, he went out to the house to confront them a day before we crossed the border. His goal was to scare them out of the neighborhood.

"There were three people inside: two females and one male. They all seemed pretty rattled. One of them had trouble remembering her name and couldn't find any identification."

A neighbor later described what happened next:

"After the cops left, Violet and her friends came running down the stairs carrying loose clothes. They threw them in the back of her convertible, jumped in, and raced off. We were glad to see them go. There were limos pulling up at all times of the night, parties that would last for days, and there were girls in slit skirts drinking martinis on the beach at dawn in the middle of the week. The Man-in-Black was creepy too; he always had an angry expression on his face and never spoke to anyone."

"The Man-in-Black?"

"Yeah, I think he's your tenant's boyfriend. I'm not sure if he was living there, but he was there a lot.

☼ ⚲ ⊙

Everyone called him that because he was always dressed in black, from head to toe, but I think his name is Luther.
Pity about that nice car too. That blonde girl left it parked outside every night with the top down – even in the pouring rain. I even said something to her about it, but she totally ignored me."

Later that day, we went out to the house. The lieutenant insisted on accompanying us in case there was any confrontation. I parked behind the green and white police cruiser across the street. From the curb, everything looked normal.

We huddled for last-minute instructions. Even though I'd given proper notice to inspect the property, per the lease agreement, it felt good to have a lawman with us.

"That's new," I said, pointing to the motion detector at the bottom of the garden stairs. "Guess they want to know when someone's coming up."

Once we reached the landing, I knocked on the front door. Then I turned to Sam and whispered, "I totally forgot that I painted the door that color... How ironic is that?"

"Shhh!" She said, jabbing me with her elbow.

Not hearing any movement, I unlocked the door and opened it. Thankfully, the locks hadn't been changed.

"Landlord, here to do inspections," I said loudly.

There was no response...

The door swung open to reveal the dining room table covered with clothes and makeup. The room had a powdery perfume scent. The windows were covered with bed sheets, making the cheery space seem dark and dreary.

There was a snake in a terrarium, tarot cards on the coffee table, and something written in lipstick on the bathroom mirror. One room had video production equipment set up in it.

☼   ⚕   ⊙

Sam kidded, "Look, someone's been shooting some home movies."

The lieutenant chuckled and made a comment I dare not repeat. As we were inspecting the property, he confided that his team had been staked out across the street in a fake cable TV van. After so many months of being parked there every day, some neighbors were convinced that Bello Beach was finally getting cable TV – only to be disappointed to learn that it wasn't.

During the investigation, the officers questioned "people of interest" as they were leaving the premises. They threatened to conduct interviews in their homes or places of work if they didn't cooperate then and there – and warned them they'd be charged with obstruction of justice if they interfered in any way.

Unsure of my involvement at first, the lieutenant questioned my neighbors about me. They all vouched for me. They knew I was off sailing – and that I'd been looking to rent the property prior to leaving. Whatever the case, he never questioned my involvement… but was curious about one thing…

"About that brass pole, was that there when you rented it?"

"Yes, I've had it for years."

"That's quite a coincidence. Not many people have brass poles in their homes."

Anticipating that question, I replied, "Yes, officer, it certainly is. My brother suggested deep cleaning the "grind zone," eighteen inches off the floor."

He laughed and bid us farewell. Alone in the house now, Sam and I continued our inspection.

"Look! A pistol! Oh my gosh, they're armed!"

"Don't touch it, Sam; you don't want your fingerprints on someone else's gun."

Outside in the garden, I found a crumpled-up piece of paper with directions to the house scribbled on it. Whoever wrote it was instructed to park on the street above mine and take the community stairs to avoid attention.

☼ ⚲ ☉

As I was emptying the ashes of the wood-burning stove, I found a partially burnt piece of paper – with either a poem or music lyrics scribbled on it about getting "higher than high before you die."

Just then the motion sensor chimed...

Sam peered out the window and exclaimed, "Oh no! There's a man coming up the stairs. I feel like we shouldn't be here right now."

"You wait in the bedroom; I'll handle this."

He inserted a key, twisted the knob, and opened the door. A dark figure in black leather stood at the threshold, looking in.

"Who the hell are you, and what are you doing in my house?" he shouted angrily.

"I'm the owner, Danny, here to inspect the property per the written notice to Violet. Who the hell are you?"

"I'm Luther; where's Violet?"

"Apparently she fled after the sheriff came by a couple of days ago. He was just here again today; as a matter of fact, you just missed him."

"Fuck off!"

"Luther, are you aware that this house has been under police surveillance for the past five months? Didn't you notice the fake cable van parked across the street?"

A look of fear swept across his face. He must have been suspicious of that vehicle. He crumbled before me.

"It wasn't me, man; I had nothing to do with it."

"Tell that to the judge."

"Please don't press charges, man. If you let me walk away, you can have my guitar and amp – and you'll never see me again."

"I don't want your stuff, Luther; I just want my house back. Can you get ahold of Violet? I need to speak with her, and she isn't answering my calls."

"Alright, I'll try, but she hasn't been answering mine either. Her phone might be turned off."

✵ 🏃 ◉

"Try calling her friends then – maybe they can help track her down."

He paced like a caged tiger on the back deck, trying to reach her. Eventually he did – and from the looks of things, their conversation was not going well. She was clearly upset that he'd spoken with me.

He screamed at her, "Shut the fuck up! I didn't say anything! Why didn't you tell me about the cops? I'm the one who should be mad!"

After concluding their heated argument, he came inside and handed me the phone.

"She wants to talk to you."

I put it to my ear.

"Sorry about the situation, Danny; apparently the people I sublet to were doing things I wasn't aware of."

"Whatever, Violet, can you please just come back here so we can work this out?"

"Why, so your cop buddies can arrest me? Sorry, Danny, that's not going to happen."

"Well, if you're not coming back, let's terminate the lease now and move your stuff out. I just want my house back."

"Alright, I'll send a truck tomorrow and have Luther load it. Can you please put him back on?"

He was sitting on the stairs with his head hanging low. I handed him the phone. They spoke briefly, then he hung up in anger.

"That bitch is staying with another guy – and she expects me to move all her shit?"

"No, Luther, I expect you to move all her shit! See you tomorrow."

The next morning, some cops showed up to question him as he was packing up. His answers were prepared, and he didn't have much to say. The brawny officer, with salt and pepper hair, advised him to be out of the house by the end of the day.

Luther was in a hateful mood. I needled him every chance I got but was mindful not to push him too far because I didn't want him to walk off the job once he realized he wasn't going to be arrested. Despite my wishes, he left his guitar and amp in the garage with a note taped to it that read:

☼ 🎣 ☉

"Sorry."

I'd successfully regained possession of the house, but it felt strange to be there. It didn't feel like home, and it sucked being the subject of neighborhood gossip. I heard everyone talking about it as they walked by.

Some neighbors, like Joey, were suspicious after the cops asked her questions about me. And my handyman, Cuco, even told me there were eight naked women hanging out watching TV one day while he was working inside. They didn't seem to mind him being there.

"Did you tell your wife about it?"

"What, and spoil a good thing? No, I just worked really slowly that day," he joked.

Later on, an acquaintance confided in me that he responded to the ad but didn't go inside when he saw that it was my house. Apparently he was too embarrassed to say anything at the time.

*I would have come straight home if any one of them had
contacted me...*

In hindsight, I'm glad they didn't...

Ignorance was bliss.

The tidbits of information I gathered helped me form a narrative. In consideration of the allegedly tawdry circumstances, it seemed entirely reasonable to withhold the security deposit to replace the locks, linens, and mattresses. After all, I had receipts for everything I replaced and had a fair amount of evidence to substantiate my case. Besides, the damages extended further than merely misuse – my neighbors, my reputation, and the value of my property had surely been affected too.

"Hopefully Violet will see this as a reasonable settlement. If she sues me and claims that she sublet it, then she'll have admitted to breaching the lease agreement."

☼ ⚔ ◉

"Just be careful, Honey. They've got a gun – and you know the history. Getting sued could be the least of your problems."

Sam was right about that, too. Violet's mother, Linda, who'd lent her daughter the money for the security deposit, was as problematic as they get.

She'd threaten me. I'd ignore her. Rinse and repeat.

Her car came to a screeching halt in front of my garage one day. Linda and her teenage son were there to collect some of Violet's remaining things that Luther left behind in the hasty move. She was surprisingly pleasant until her son carried a box down to the car and could no longer hear us.

"If you don't return the entire deposit, you'll be sorry."

"Violet will get back exactly what she deserves."

"Every penny, Danny," she snarled, "every penny!"

The tense days that followed culminated when one of her family members, a convicted murderer, contacted me and demanded that the money be returned. Now I was sideways with a killer whose son, incidentally, was convicted of brutally murdering his girlfriend a few years later.

"How much further would this escalate?" I asked myself.
"Is this going to turn out badly?"

☼ ⚲ ☉

Chapter 33
The Surprise

After a week of sleeping with a loaded shotgun beside my bed in case I needed to defend myself in the middle of the night, tensions began to ease. I knew it wasn't over, but everything felt calmer.

"Let's head to Europe. This incident can't derail our adventure."

"Really?" Sam probed, trying to gauge my resolve.

"Absolutely. We can't squander this opportunity just because we had a bad experience. Remember how rattled we were after the big storm off Baja? Well, this is just another type of storm. We'll recover from this too."

Eager to see Europe for the first time, Sam started jumping for joy.

Luckily, some neighbors introduced us to a family of educators on summer break who were interested in housesitting. After I told them everything that had happened, Alec turned to his wife, Colleen, to gauge her reaction. Although she looked concerned, their two little girls in swimsuits and flip-flops showed no reservations at all. Sensing their parents' reluctance to close the deal, they clung to their legs and begged.

"Can we please stay at the beach, Mommy and Daddy? Pleeease?"

Colleen acquiesced, "Well, I'm sure it will be fine. If they haven't come back by now, I doubt they'll come back at all."

It was nice to have a sweet family staying in the house. After handing them the keys, Sam and I drove to my parents' house since they were giving us a ride to the airport the following day. We were both excited about Europe.

"Hey Sammi, let's agree not to talk about what happened back home during our tour. The house is safe, and we have a whole continent to explore. Let's enjoy the adventure and not dwell on the past."

She smiled and replied, "I love that idea; nothing's going to bring us down."

That afternoon, we took my metallic green tandem bicycle, named Greeny, on a shakedown cruise to test the new components. We pushed the

☼ 🏃 ◉

fully loaded bike across country roads at a brisk pace; it had the stability of a motorcycle. Satisfied with the performance, we disassembled it and packed the parts in an oversized tandem box – made from two bike boxes duct-taped together.

The next day, just as we were about to leave for the airport, I received a call from Colleen.

"I just wanted to wish you a good trip, and don't worry, we'll take great care of..."

She stopped mid-sentence. I could hear her talking with Alec in the background. Suddenly, there was panic in their voices.

Colleen returned to the phone with troubling news: "Danny, I think your tenants are back. Alec just said there are some people trying to get into the garage."

"Well, they won't have much luck. I changed the keypad combination."

"Alec, please come inside right now!" she pleaded.

Too late, he'd already descended the stairs to confront them.

"Can I help you?" he asked.

Violet and Luther seemed startled. "Um, we heard this house is for rent, and we're interested in renting it."

A minute later, he returned and picked up the phone.

"Hey Danny. Crisis averted, I guess. They got back in their car when I told them that we'd already called the cops."

"Thanks Alec. They're probably just here to pick up some music equipment they left behind."

Then Colleen shouted in the background, "Oh no, now a man is coming up the stairs!"

Knock, knock, knock.

"Please don't open the door," I pleaded to no avail.

Too late, Alec already had. I strained to hear the faint conversation. The door closed. A few seconds later, Alec returned to the phone.

☼ 🏃 ☉

"Is everything alright?" I asked anxiously.

"Yeah," he said, sounding relieved, "they just handed me some papers."

"Papers? What papers?"

He shuffled through them before breaking the bad news: "Sorry, Danny, it looks like you're being sued."

Chapter 34
The Next Flight to Brussels

Assembling a tandem bicycle in an airport is never an easy task. Having done it several times before, I dreaded the process. Viciously grumpy from a sleepless flight, I barked profanities each time I skinned a knuckle. Once finished, I jammed my bloody digits into my cycling gloves and trumpeted my success.

"I'm done!"

"Heard that before," Sam snickered. "Are we really ready to go this time?"

"Absolutely…well, except for…wait a minute," I muttered as I started readjusting the packs.

"Are you sure this bike isn't overloaded? It looks ridiculous."

"I'll have you know that I've taken this bike on several tours with these very same packs. It's balanced and sturdy…"

"…and looks ridiculous," Sam giggled. "Will it even fit on a bike path?"

Fully-loaded Greeny on the Mosel Radweg

Indeed, our bulging steed would draw commentary across the continent. We had all the things two people would need for an extended bikepacking tour, including front and rear bike bags, known as panniers, a handlebar bag, and a rear rack with a tent, sleeping bags, sleeping pads, towels, and a spare tire bungeed atop it.

Much of the ninety-pound load was attributed to spare parts and special tools needed for the tandem. The combined weight of two riders and their heavy packs devours drive trains and wheels. Since tandem bike parts are hard to find, it was wise to carry a full set of spares.

In 2004, tandems were a rare sight in Europe, typically reserved for the legally blind or assumingly gay – as evidenced by the line of questioning Tim and I got from a little old lady while touring Germany:

> *"Excuse me, do you ride a two-person bike because one of you is blind?"*
>
> *"No, we ride a tandem because it's the best way to tour. You can cover a lot more ground than on a regular bike, and its fun to stay together," Tim replied.*
>
> *She peered over her thick bifocals, down at our Lycra shorts, and asked, "Und you two are also a tandem?"*

Sam and I pushed the lumbering bike to the curb outside baggage claim and straddled it. Captain Dan and Stoker Sam swerved into the congested traffic and followed the signs to "Brussels City Centre." It was exhilarating to embark upon another adventure – especially on such a perfect summer day.

We barreled into Brussels with the bell ringing. Mounted on the stoker's handlebar, it's primarily rung to say, "Get out of the way," in any language – it can also be used to greet people we pass, as motivation on a grueling climb, or like this time – out of pure joy. If it's rung for the latter, it's customary for the captain to slip their palm back to the stoker to have it slapped in acknowledgement of the awesomeness. And, of course, the captain can request it at any time by calling out, "Bell!"

☼   🚶   ☉

"I'm ready for a Por qué no."

"Already?" Sam protested. "We just left the airport."

"Exactly my point; let's celebrate that."

Glimpsing a Pilsner glass at an outdoor cafe, I slammed on the brakes. I was immediately reminded how ineffective rim-clinching brakes are on a mass with such inertia, even in dry conditions. On a fully loaded tandem, wanting to stop and being stopped are two very different things.

To slow the four hundred pounds of combined weight, capable of careening down mountainsides at over seventy miles an hour, Greeny is equipped with a drag-brake on the rear axle. This drum brake technology is an essential component for controlling speed, especially on long downhill grades where the heat induced by rim-clinching brakes can cause the skinny tires to blow out.

The drum brake provides a steady and reliable drag. Once set, the bike will creep down even the steepest grades without accelerating – even in wet and icy conditions. It also serves as an excellent parking brake and theft deterrent because the bike won't budge when it's set. Although the brake lever is mounted on the stoker's handlebar, the captain can request it at any time by calling out, "Brake!"

After we came to a stop, we dismounted, leaned the bike against a wall, and sat at an empty table.

"Are they ever going to take our order?" I whined impatiently after failing to get a waiter's attention. "Do you think they're refusing to serve us because of the way we're dressed?"

"Well, everyone's all dressed up here, we're in bike clothes, and you have grease on your face," she said as she pawed it away.

We expected lousy table service in Europe, but the wait staff at this establishment seemed to be intentionally avoiding us.

"If there's anything Grouchy has taught me, it's that when the going gets tough, the tough get annoying. Watch this…"

"Oh no, here we go again…"

Sam picked up her helmet and gloves and started walking to the bike. She knew better than to look back.

☼ ⚲ ◉

Ignore the ugly American at table fourteen…

Back on the road, I lamented leaving Mexico – no doubt suffering from culture shock. The beautiful people in the fancy brasseries took life way too seriously, in my opinion – ideologically opposite to our flip-flop and floatie-raft lifestyle aboard Marylee. They were the antithesis of cruisers.

Europe is an outstanding place for cycling, though. The charming cobblestone city centers give way to scenic bike paths that traverse the undulating countryside. Belgium's outstanding cycling infrastructure and gentle rolling hills made it a perfect place to begin our journey. It's always a good idea to spend a couple weeks touring in the lowlands to get leaner, stronger, and fitter before reaching the steep grades of the Alps.

We rode through fields of flowers, lush forests, and quaint hamlets – and crossed numerous bridges spanning olive-green canals. The reality of being in Europe was starting to sink in.

"This is so different from the barrenness of Baja, huh, Sammi?"

"I love it here. Everything's so green."

"You'll like camping in Europe too. The campgrounds here usually have great amenities. I prefer to stealth-camp near one, and just pay to use the facilities. That way you can have privacy – and still have hot showers in the morning. Stealth-camping will also allow us to ride until we're tired each day. We'll just pitch a tent behind a bush without cost or reservations. If the weather gets bad, we'll get a hotel room – I promise you that."

"Fine by me, I'd rather sleep under the stars if the weather is nice anyway."

The only mishap I've had while stealth-camping was with my buddy, Pat, after we pitched our tents at night on the outskirts of Zurich.

"Dan, wake up," he said, jiggling my tent.

"What's up?" I yawned as I poked my head out, squinting in the morning sun.

☼   🏃   ◉

"Dude, we camped in some lady's backyard – and she's waving for us to come up to the house. I can't believe we didn't see it last night. What do you want to do?"

The sweet Swiss lady on the terrace was torn between whether to call the police or invite us inside for breakfast. Thankfully, she did the latter. Although it turned out to be a memorable experience, it's not one I wish to repeat. It taught me to settle in before sundown – when you can still see all your surroundings.

After riding forty miles north, our excitement gave way to jetlag. We felt haggard and craved hot showers, so I went into the administration office of an expansive park to see if there was a campground nearby. A fit Jamaican in his mid-twenties was eager to assist.

He walked me outside, jumped on a beach cruiser, and motioned for us to follow him, "Dis' way, mon."

He took off with his dreadlocks whipping in the wind; we struggled to keep up with him. Eventually he stopped at the edge of the park, where he waited for us to catch up.

"Dere's camping ober dere, mon," he said, pointing to a sloppily painted sign across the street that read "Camping."

We thanked him, dismounted Greeny, and walked her toward the entrance.

"Gee, mon," I whispered, "this place looks like a gypsy camp. If we stay here, we'll likely get robbed."

"Well, it's only for one night, and I'm too exhausted to look for another spot. Let's take a shower, grab some dinner, and crash. We can keep our valuables with us and lock the bike to the tent while we sleep."

"This is exactly how horror movies begin: "Two weary travelers…""

"What are you so concerned about? You were just sleeping in a suspected brothel with a loaded shotgun beside your bed."

☼ ⚲ ⊙

Although she had a fair point, she knew that comment would sting.

After pitching the tent and taking a coin-operated shower, we rode into town for a Flemish dinner without any packs on Greeny. My, how nimble she felt without the extra weight. We dined on Vlaamse Frites (french-fries smothered in mayonnaise) and Belgian chocolates – and washed it all down with Dutch beer. Thankfully, we returned to our sketchy campsite before the evil clowns came out.

Although I was exhausted, I was too excited to sleep. Our journey across Europe was underway. I stayed awake thinking about how much better our first day was compared to the first day of my 1,700-mile tour from Canada to Mexico with my buddy, Rob:

> *Our mishap began where many mishaps do – in a bar. After some "arrival beers" in the Vancouver Airport, we climbed aboard Greeny – a bike we specifically purchased for the trip, because we knew as competitive cyclists we'd be racing each other all day on single bikes. Although there's more control as captain, we both enjoyed being the stoker because you're free to relax, snap pictures, and even roll a joint.*
>
> *Just after leaving the airport, we somehow missed the "No Bikes Allowed" sign and began plummeting into a tunnel that led us under the estuary south of the city. It was the idiotic equivalent of riding a bicycle through New York's Holland Tunnel during rush hour.*
>
> *Without a shoulder, we were forced to ride in a lane with cars on our rear wheel as we dove deeper into the black abyss. There were metal grates every 100-feet with slippery wheel-eating gaps. Surely we'd crash and be crushed by the traffic...it was only a matter of time.*
>
> *After several scary slides, we reached the bottom of the tunnel and began climbing out. The cars directly*

☼ 🏃 ⊙

*behind us began swerving around us as we slowed –
opening us up to speeding vehicles that weren't aware a
bicycle was in the tunnel. The darkness was our doom.*

*"Give me your light!" I called to Rob, who was
captain at the time.*

*He ripped the headlight from his handlebar and
passed it back to me. I began waving it at the cars behind
us – causing all lanes of traffic to slow down to match our
speed.*

*In the distance, we saw sunlight. Eventually we
exited the tunnel with bumper-to-bumper traffic on our
wheel. We pulled over and dismounted to regain
composure. As soon as we began pedaling again, we heard
a siren behind us.*

*"Crap, we're getting pulled over," Rob
announced.*

*"You've got to be kidding me," I grumbled as we
slowed to a stop.*

*A moose-sized Mountie with a handlebar
mustache climbed out of his cruiser and approached us.*

*"Congratulations, gentlemen – you're celebrities.
Every TV and radio station in Vancouver is talking about
the cyclists that backed up rush hour traffic all the way
into downtown."*

*We apologized, pleaded ignorance, and begged
for leniency. We told him that we'd just begun a highly
anticipated bike tour. Showing compassion, the way
Canadians always do, he let us off easy.*

*"I'm a biker too, eh," he said, handing us a yellow
ticket, "so you're only getting a warning this time. You
guys need to be more careful though...at least until you're
over the border."*

Chapter 35
Amsterdamn

The next morning, we awoke refreshed and recharged – ready to pedal across Belgium. We boarded our glistening steed, dotted with morning dew, as the sun began to rise. It was exhilarating to dash across the countryside and barnstorm the blooming villages at such high rates of speed.

We arrived in Antwerp by midday, where we found the streetcar tracks around Centraal Station to be extremely slippery on skinny bike tires. We rode through the adjacent gem district, where Hasidic Jews wearing dark overcoats and brimmed hats are known for trading diamonds with merely a handshake.

As much as we enjoyed Belgium, the Netherlands beckoned – the most bike-friendly country in the world. It took a couple of days to reach Amsterdam, a circus of concentric circles with more canals than Venice. You never know what to expect there. On my first visit, Dam Square was overrun with thousands of Hare Krishnas dancing around with tambourines and scaling the seventy-two foot obelisk.

Since bike theft is perpetually at epidemic proportions in Amsterdam, we needed a secure place to store Greeny while we were in museums, restaurants, and coffeeshops. We looked for a budget-friendly hotel between Vondelpark and Leidseplein that would allow us to bring our bike into the room. Keeping it close was our only chance of keeping it. I remembered the stern warning I got the last time I had Greeny in this town:

> *"Even if you lock that bike to your dick, it will be gone by morning."*

Amsterdam's tall, narrow buildings, built that way because property owners were taxed on street frontage, are particularly difficult for

☼   🚶   ☉

oversized bikes. They simply won't fit around tight stairways – even with both wheels off.

After a long search, we finally found a hotel with a room on the ground floor with a solid radiator to lock Greeny to. It was nice to be off the bike after several days of riding. Our legs felt rubbery and sore.

Of all the museums in Europe, Van Gogh is my personal favorite. I was excited to take Sam there. After seeing so many prints, it's wonderful to see the textured originals in person. Arranged chronologically, the museum gives insight into the painter's personal life and mental state. The warm hues and pastel colors of happier times gave way to the dark and menacing images when the painter was manically depressed.

Off the bike in Amsterdam

We stumbled upon the privately-owned torture museum later that night. There are macabre lithographs hanging next to each apparatus, depicting how the machine was used on its subjects. It's a creepy place full of small rooms with dimly lit red lights – with a moaning and groaning soundtrack playing in the background to enhance the experience. Collected from dungeons all over Europe, there are racks, stocks, cages, guillotines, and spiked chairs everywhere.

One of the most excruciating devices, and perhaps the simplest, was called the genuflector. It simply handcuffs the victim's wrists and ankles together – causing their organs to kink and eventually fail. It was considered one of the most dreaded forms of death, probably because it took so long to die. The most disturbing machine, though, was the splaying machine – where the subjects were forced to watch their innards being wound on a large wooden spool in front of them.

When we realized that the museum had closed for the evening, and that we were all alone on the sixth floor, we began to feel anxious.

"What kind of person works in a torture museum anyway?" I kidded with Sam. "And what happens to straggling tourists?"

"I don't know, and I'm not going to find out. I'm outta here, Buster."

I reflected on the Netherlands' sensible approach to prostitution – and how sex workers were kept safe in a controlled environment. Since it's going to happen anyway, at least it's kept out of unsuspecting neighborhoods – like mine.

As enjoyable as it was, three days in Amsterdam were plenty. Like an overstayed carnival, the novelty had worn-off. Ready to ramble, we rode off into the countryside. There were so many great places to see, and such great distances between them.

The further southeast we rode, the hillier the terrain became. I was pleased with the new mountain bike gearing I'd installed before the trip; it made the steep grades much easier to climb. We stealth-camped in secluded forests and on grassy riverbanks; however, I was careful where I peed after the trauma that befell my brother:

> *On a tandem tour from Amsterdam to Munich, Tim and I pitched a tent on the outskirts of a small village and walked through the woods into town for dinner. After eating, we adjourned to the bar.*
> *"Ver are you staying?" a blond man asked.*

☼   🕺   ⊙

"At the campground outside of town," Tim replied.

"Ha!" he hooted. *"A vasp is going to sting your dick. A vasp is going to sting your dick."*

We laughed it off, but he kept repeating it throughout the evening. When the shrooms came on, we bolted for the door – surely there'd be trolls to battle in the forest.

There was a final "Vasp, dick!" as the door closed behind us.

"I had to get out of there," Tim huffed. *"That guy wouldn't stop talking. Heard you the first time…"*

Pity Tim didn't heed all those warnings. When he got out of the tent to go pee the next morning, the screams were incredible.

☼ 🕴 ⊙

Chapter 36
Fantasyland

The Grand Duchy of Luxembourg is one of the smallest countries in continental Europe. It's an upscale place where stately manors sit between rolling green vineyards bordered by tall trees. The duchy's nominal breadth was no match for our ravenous tandem; we blazed through the countryside in a single day – rolling into Luxembourg City around suppertime.

Spotting a Chinese restaurant, Sam slammed on the drag-brake. After pedaling sixty-five hilly miles, we were famished. We locked up our bulging bike, where we could see it from a window, and went inside the fancy establishment.

We ordered an obnoxious amount of food; so much that our waitress began to giggle. We ordered so much that they had to pull up a second table to accommodate all the dishes. So amused by our appetites were the Chinese wait staff, they rooted for us to finish – as if we were in a pie-eating contest.

"Wow, you very hungry!"

"Best Chinese food ever," I said, sucking a chow mein noodle into my mouth.

Sam grunted something in response, but it was entirely intelligible. From the expression on her face, gnawing on a pork rib like a sub-Saharan jackal, she obviously agreed.

After the meal, we were so bloated that we had trouble getting back on the bike. Like an engorged tick with limited mobility, I used my hand to lift my leg over the top tube. Eventually, we slipped off into the night in search of a flat spot to pitch our tent.

We came upon a dusty forest across from the country's only commercial airport. It was by no means ideal. The forest floor was rocky, covered with dead branches, and on an incline. We were too tired to look

☼ 🚶 ◉

for another campsite, though, so we cleared the site as best we could and collapsed on the uneven ground.

"I didn't sleep a wink on that woodpile," Sam moaned as she rubbed her stiff neck the next morning.

Considering how little we slept, we felt surprisingly refreshed – a sign that our metabolism was speeding up. After riding all day, every day, you tend to need less and less sleep. That's a good thing when living in a tent because the sun often chases you out early anyway.

We chowed on Chinese leftovers before hitting the road at daybreak. My windbreaker whipped as we plummeted into the gorge that cradled the river below. The scene looked like a train set, too charming to be real. Sam rang the bell for joy as we sped down the slope at over sixty miles an hour.

Eventually we reached the valley floor where the Mosel River enters Germany. Familiar with this stretch, having ridden it before, I was thrilled to be back on my favorite bike path in Europe – the unrivaled Mosel Radweg. Of all the Fahrradtours I've taken, the stretch from Trier to Koblenz is my all-time favorite.

Germany's impressive network of freshly paved bicycle highways, known as "Radwegs," are perhaps the safest and most extensive in the world. Over two hundred routes crisscross the countryside, filled with medieval castles, deep forests, and fairytale villages. In urban areas, they have off-ramps, overpasses, tunnels, and an impressive amount of well-lit signage – making them effectively Autobahns for bicycles.

Germany is also one of the best countries in Europe in terms of travel value. Prices are reasonable compared to neighboring countries for high quality goods and services and hearty portions of food and drink.

The tiny villages along the Mosel are so dolled up you'd swear you were in a theme park. The cobblestone streets, gingerbread houses, blooming gardens, and quaint festivals are so innocently endearing that you'd swear you stepped back in time.

"It feels like we're in a fairytale," Sam said.

"That's because most of the fairytales you've known since you were a child – Rapunzel, Snow White, Rumpelstiltskin, Hansel and Gretel,

Cinderella, and Sleeping Beauty were all written by the Brothers Grimm not far from here."

In the Roman city of Trier, the oldest city in Germany, the central square was packed with tourists eating at outdoor cafes. Just as we sat down at a table, a Dixieland jazz band began playing to a plaza filled with dancers.

"Dixieland? I was kind of hoping for an oom-pah band," Sam pouted.

I didn't hear a word she said. All I cared about was the beer the waiter had just delivered.

"Ah, mother's milk," I said, smacking my lips, "it's a perfect Pilsner."

"Oh my gosh. That's the best beer I've ever tasted, and I don't even like beer."

"You know, Ben Franklin once said, 'Beer is proof that God loves us.' If that's true, God sure loves Germany."

The country's affinity for brewing dates back to the Deutsche Rheinheitsgebaut, a German purity law passed in the Duchy of Bavaria in 1516 that mandated strict cleanliness and quality guidelines for the monk-run Brauereis. For centuries, the end result has been beer so pure and fresh that it rarely causes hangovers. And like a pint of Guinness in Ireland, German beers taste much better in Germany.

After blowing the froth off a couple, we hopped back on the bike and pedaled east in the warm sunshine. We rode through the vineyards, interspersed with apple, plum, and cherry orchards, back and forth across the ancient stone bridges that span the river.

In a flat spot near the picturesque hamlet of Issel, a large festival was unfurling. The 2004 Mosel River Valley Harvest Festival was about to get underway. We rolled in just as the beer and wine casks were being tapped. We stopped our steed, pitched a tent on the enormous lawn, and joined the party.

The region is famous for Rieslings, some of Germany's finest white wines, ranging from sugar-sweet dessert wines to dry and crisp varietals. Many of the local wineries, or "Weinguts," had wine tasting stands set up around the massive bar in the middle.

"This is the largest wine festival in Germany," the bartender pronounced. "It's considered the Oktoberfest of wine."

"How about that, Sammi? If everything goes as planned, we'll be at the Oktoberfest of beer in a few months too. It's nice to know we aren't missing any parties."

The crowd grew thicker as the evening progressed, and a rock band started to play. There were carnival rides and games of chance, including a dart toss to win a long-stemmed rose.

Sam liked that idea. "I'd rather win a rose than a cheap stuffed animal any day."

The fireworks display was a pyrotechnic masterpiece – illuminating the valley for miles in either direction. The scent of sulfur was so strong that it burned our sinuses. For the grand finale, a tall-masted ship was set ablaze on the river, which caused the crowd to cheer.

We met some guys who were intrigued by our trip and likely interested in Sam, that invited us to go out on their speedboat the following day.

After the heat drove us out of our tent the next morning, we were squinting and stretching in the morning sun.

"What a crazy night."

"Yeah, that was a blast," Sam said in a raspy voice. "Hey, didn't we agree to go out on a boat today?"

"Yeah, but it's ten o'clock already; they're probably already gone."

It wasn't surprising that they waited for us; there's no such thing as an empty promise in Germany. The lounge chairs on the foredeck provided the perfect platform for viewing castles and wildlife. A whiteness of swans paddled by.

Back on the bike by the afternoon, we decided to slow the pace down and spend more time savoring the surroundings. After averaging seventy miles a day for the past two weeks, it felt good to lounge on the grassy banks and swim in the cool water.

       ☼   ⚲   ◉

Stopping for a swim on the Mosel

Most days we'd eat fresh pastries from a Backerei for breakfast, stop at an outdoor café for lunch, have beer and ice cream at a Biergarten in the afternoon, and snack in the tent before going to bed. We needed to consume an enormous amount of calories each day; otherwise, our blood sugar would drop and we'd "bonk" even when we weren't riding.

> *The worst bonking episode I'd ever experienced was on the tour from Canada to Mexico. Despite eating four huge meals and nine energy bars, the mountainous 145-mile leg down the Big Sur coast had taken its toll. Rob started talking gibberish and laughing uncontrollably for no reason. That experience made me realize another benefit of a tandem bicycle: you can designate a driver if one rider becomes impaired.*

Aside from the excruciating leg cramps at night, we felt stronger with each passing day. The physical transformation from cruiser to transcontinental cyclist was evident. Riding all day afforded us the unique ability to eat whatever we wanted and still lose weight – a splendid way to see Europe.

We meandered through the orchards and vineyards each day, where friendly farmers invited us to pick fruit from their trees while they admired our machine. Tandems make everyone happy.

In Germany, camping is generally tolerated, and eco-adventuring is encouraged. This made it easy for us to pitch our tent on the river's grassy banks, preferably within walking distance of a restaurant where Bier is cheaper than bottled water.

We'd swim in the river each morning and eat breakfast on the banks – stretched out with a map to discuss the logistics of the day. The only nights we stayed in designated campgrounds were when we needed to do laundry.

> *Riding through Bernkastel-Kues reminded me of the time Tim and I befriended a fellow cyclist at a Tankestelle bicycle wine bar on the side of the Radweg. To his wife's chagrin, he invited us to stay the night in their guest bedroom – and even treated us to a pork shank dinner at the restaurant she worked at. There, he told the legend of Doctor Lösing, the creator of Eiswein.*
>
> *Apparently Lösing's ultra-sweet dessert wine, made from harvesting grapes immediately after they freeze, cured a sick princess in the castle above town – thereby making him a doctor.*
>
> *Few regions in the world have the conditions to create Eiswein, where the grapes freeze just as they reach peak sugar content. Even there, the conditions must be perfect. Some years, it doesn't happen at all.*

☼ ⛵ ☉

Continuing east toward Koblenz, we reached the walled city of Cochem with its regal castle, Schloss Reichsburg, perched high on a hill above the town below. First constructed around 1000 A.D., this neo-gothic fortress, restored in the eighteenth century, is glimmering and pristine. In the summertime, it's packed with tourists snapping photos of the castle and wandering through the cobblestone streets of the Altstadt.

"Do you think the rest of our ride will be as amazing as the last week has been?" Sam asked over an afternoon ice cream sundae.

"The Mosel is going to be tough to beat, especially after the perfect weather we've had. Don't worry though, there are plenty of majestic mountains and warm Italian beaches ahead of us."

"I guess so, but I could stay here all summer."

The fairytale came to an abrupt end shortly after we checked into a hotel in Koblenz, where we had internet access for the first time since Amsterdam.

"Bad news, Sammi. I got an email from the court informing me that Violet has moved up the appearance date. Now it's scheduled for two weeks from today."

"Isn't there any way you can change it back to November? That doesn't seem fair."

"I'll call the court on Monday and see – but if I don't show up, she'll automatically win. I can't let that happen; I need to defend myself."

"Do you think she moved up the date because she's trying to ruin our trip?"

"I doubt it; she probably just wants to expedite things. I'd do the same thing if I were in her shoes."

The news affected our mood as we rolled down the Rhine that weekend.

Sam growled, "I feel like there's a dark cloud hanging over us – always threatening to rain on our trip. You know, I really regret baking them an apple pie."

Chapter 37
The Donau Radweg

Stealth-camping on the Rhine

From our campsite overlooking the Rhine, I called the county court offices from my satellite phone as soon as they opened on Monday. The helpful clerk had good news: "Each party is allowed to change the appearance date once. Since the plaintiff has already moved it, you're entitled to move it as well – but keep in mind that neither party will be able to change it after that."

"Does that mean we'll be able to move it back to November?"

"That shouldn't be a problem. You'll have to fill out a form and pay a fee, but we'll be happy to accommodate your request."

When I shared the news with Sam, that our trip would continue as planned, she began dancing around the campsite.

The next day, we took a riverboat down the castle-studded Rhine to celebrate. We toasted tall Pilsners from lounge chairs on the deck.

"Cheers, Rabbit Ears."

"Now this is top living," Sam giggled.

By the time we disembarked at Rüdesheim it was raining, so we hopped a train to Würzburg since the weather was better to the east. Our policy of taking alternative forms of transportation in inclement weather paid off nicely on several occasions. There's no shame in taking the train; it's a vacation, not a death march. I learned this the hard way on other tours by forcing myself to ride every mile through all sorts of traffic and weather. By now I realized what really mattered was that we were safe, comfortable, and enjoying ourselves.

After the train screeched to a stop in Würzburg, we rolled Greeny out of the bicycle carriage and through the train station, where several people stopped to admire her. It was hot and humid outside, but at least it was dry.

As the sun began to set, we strapped some sausages and sauerkraut to the tandem's rear rack and raced off to find a campsite before it got dark. Eventually we found a flat spot on a grassy lawn under a weeping willow. After a quick meal in the tent, we drifted off to sleep.

The next morning we were awakened by someone shouting, "Schlaffen Sie gut?"

"What the heck is that?" I said, unzipping my sleeping bag to investigate. "Is someone yelling at us?"

"Wake up!" someone else yelled.

When I poked my head out of the tent, I had a sinking realization that we'd camped on a lawn of the University of Würzburg and were now surrounded by students going to class. Their taunts were relentless.

Despite being heckled, we were determined to stay nestled in our silky warm sleeping bags for as long as we could – so we stuck our earplugs in and slept for another hour.

We packed our tent in record time, embarrassingly in front of a student audience, and set off for Passau – a hundred miles to the east.

Situated on the German, Czech, and Austrian borders, Passau is a cultural crossroads of great strategic importance. Located where the Inn and Danube Rivers converge, it's long been a hub of regional commerce.

The magnificent Danube, or "der Donau," is the second longest navigable waterway in Europe – stretching 1,200-miles from Germany to

☼ 🕴 ⊙

the Black Sea. The fast-moving, chilly green water wasn't as pleasant to swim in as the Mosel, but the lush forests and rugged mountain scenery made up for it. Atop its grassy banks is one of the most beloved bike paths in the world, the Donau Radweg.

This particular Radweg draws cyclists from all around the world each summer, making it feel like a cruising ground for bikes. We met interesting people along the way as we progressed roughly at the same pace. It seemed like everyone camped in the same campgrounds, ate at the same cafés, and drank at the same Biergartens. Before long, we'd given nicknames to some of the familiar faces.

"There goes Squeaky," I said as the guy needing chain lube passed by our table at an outdoor café.

"Stinky rode by while you were in the bathroom," Sam added, referring to the guy that wore the same jersey every day.

As we progressed east, the area became more rustic and remote – with an occasional farm carved-out of the timbered hillsides.

"I'm ready for some ice cream," Sam said. "It's about that time of day…"

"Me too, but I doubt we'll find anything around here."

Thirty seconds later, we came upon a six-foot freestanding ice cream cone sign in front of a large chalet.

"Well, I'll be. Maybe they've got cold beer too?"

Indeed, they did. As it turned out, we'd stumbled onto an immaculate campground with all the amenities. After surveying the available campsites that overlooked the river, we decided to wedge ourselves in between two campervans. A handsome couple in their mid-sixties sat on lawn chairs next to the one with Italian plates. They both had a tall glass of red wine in their hands.

"Buena Serra," the man said in a deep Italian accent, "you speak-a English?"

"Yes, we're Americans, from California."

They burst out in laughter.

"Your bike-a is-a so big-a. Where you go on such-a big-a bike-a?"

☼ 🕇 ◉

"We're riding it all around Europe. We started in Brussels and are headed to Italy and then back up to Oktoberfest before we fly home."

They howled with laughter. Apparently our plan was preposterous to them. They laughed so hard and for so long that Sam and I awkwardly started laughing with them.

"You ride-a that-a big-a bike-a in Italia, your-a gonna die-a!" the lady warned.

He concurred, "Si, Italia no good-a for big-a bike-a, your-a gonna die-a."

They went on to describe all the ways in which we would meet our fate. Between the narrow shoulders, careless drivers, and summertime tourist traffic, it sounded like we were gonna die-a. They advised us to stay north of Italy but sensed our reluctance to heed their warnings. They probably said a rosary on our behalf after we departed, piously praying for safe passage.

"Wow, this is the best goulash soup I've ever had," Sam declared from the panoramic terrace, "and I've had a lot of goulash soup lately."

Even though the campground was exceptional, we needed to keep moving. Perhaps more so than sailing, on a bicycle there's an insatiable appetite to see what's around the next bend.

The evergreen forest next to the ever-widening river gave way to agricultural plains as we pushed east toward Linz. There, in the flatlands, we encountered tremendous headwinds that halved our speed and doubled the effort. Anabatic in nature, they'd stiffen in the late afternoon and die just after sunset. After two days of fighting them, we decided to adjust our riding schedule to avoid them as much as possible.

We stopped at a family campground near Mauthausen, complete with a pool, waterslides, and riverfront bar. There were children everywhere enjoying their summer vacation.

"Everyone in America has a swimming pool," one boy informed his father just before jumping in.

I caught a glimpse of myself in a full-length mirror. The weight I'd put on in Mexico, from my decadent cruiser lifestyle, had mostly melted away. None of my pants fit anymore.

☼   ⚲   ◉

"You look healthier, and I should know because, as stoker, I'm looking at your butt all day," Sam said as she playfully pinched it.

"Sailing and cycling are perfectly paired – one makes you fat, and one makes you fit."

Although we anticipated losing weight, we were surprised at how quickly it happened considering the enormous amount of crap we were eating. Our bodies were furnaces that incinerated everything instantly, no matter how horrible it was for us.

Like on the boat, we had also become a highly synchronized team. On a tandem, it's normal to feel vibrations run through the frame as the captain and stoker become acquainted with one another, but after months of pedaling in balanced unison, the bike becomes an extension of the riders. We were so smooth and steady by Austria that sometimes I wondered if Sam was still onboard.

The region we were in was reminiscent of the Netherlands, with high levee banks on either side of the river and bike paths atop them. The river stilled just upstream of each lock.

"Hey look, Honey, it's Swan Lake," I said as we rode past a bevy.

As the distances between goods and services increased the further eastward we pushed, we became more reliant on the supplies we carried with us. On a lonely stretch outside Krems, we became desperate for food and water after ten hours of riding. There was no sign of civilization in any direction. The endless miles of levee banks and impenetrable forests sank our morale.

"I'm starving," Sam moaned. "Is there any food left?"

"Unfortunately not. We're out of food and water. I can't believe we've gone through it all."

"I feel like I'm going to pass out. Are there any towns nearby?"

"There's nothing close on the map. This area must be a flood zone – just look at how high the levee banks are. I thought we'd find something by now, but we haven't even seen a house in twenty-five miles."

"I need to stop," Sam said a few miles later. "I don't feel well."

☼ ⚲ ☉

"I'm burnt too, Sammi, but we've got to keep riding. There's nowhere to camp, and even if there was, we still need to find food and water. We'll be miserable and won't sleep a wink if we don't find both."

We pushed our depleted bodies fifteen miles further. It was dark and cold, and we were becoming edgy.

Sam suddenly stopped pedaling and said, "I just can't go on any further, even if it means sleeping on the bike path."

As we were coasting to a stop, we spotted a light on the horizon. We agreed to ride to it, whatever it was, and ask for help. We needed help.

As we got closer, we were overjoyed to see that it was a riverside Imbiss snack bar – with sausages grilling over an open fire. We were literally trembling with hunger – ready to faint. Neither of us had ever bonked that badly.

We devoured a massive amount of food in a short amount of time – like we'd been pulled from a life raft after a week of starving at sea. The sweet ladies working there were concerned with our condition. After initially telling us there were no hotels in the vicinity, they began pouring through a phone book and making calls to find us lodging. They were going to find us a warm room, even if that meant taking us into their own homes.

Eventually they found a vacancy in a nearby winery that rented rooms. They wrote down instructions on how to get there and handed it to us. When we rode up to the enormous front gate, a handsome young man greeted us and escorted us to our immaculate five-bedroom suite with a chef's kitchen and whirlpool tub.

He explained that the rooms were individually rented and shared the large common space, but since there were no other guests that evening, it was all ours for €25. He invited us to help ourselves to the refrigerator full of chilled wines and fresh cider, and promised us a big breakfast in the morning.

As soon as he left, Sam cranked up the heat, poured a glass of white wine, and took a long bubble bath.

"And you wanted to sleep on the bike path…" I ribbed.

☼ 𝓴 ◉

The next morning, an elderly lady on a beach cruiser stopped to admire our bike. She told us that the entire area had been under twenty feet of water twice in the past five years. You certainly wouldn't know it, as with everything in Austria, the buildings were freshly painted and picture-perfect.

Back on the Radweg, we discussed our plight the previous evening.

"I feel like we were saved last night," Sam sighed. "I've never been so exhausted in my life. Thank God for those ladies at the snack bar – they were so good to us."

"We were lucky to find food when we did. From now on, let's carry more emergency provisions on those long stretches."

As we rounded a sweeping river bend, in the distance we could see Vienna's mirrored skyscrapers piercing the forest canopy that carpets the city below.

"Look, it's the Emerald City."

"That's funny; it kinda does look like Oz," Sam giggled. "If that's the Emerald City, then the Donau Radweg must be the yellow brick road. The gravel is kinda yellow."

We started singing, "Follow, follow, follow, follow the yellow gravel Radweg."

Austria's affinity for music and the fine arts is second to none. Vienna pulses with it. It seems that every citizen has mastered at least one instrument, and is accomplished in several others. Classical music rifts through the streets like no other place in the world. It's so woven into the fabric of Austrian society that it's not uncommon to have a train, bus, or gondola spontaneously erupt into an impromptu jam session.

It was the Hapsburgs' love for music that advanced it more than any monarchy in history during their 650-year rule of the Austro-Hungarian Empire. Mozart, Beethoven, Brahms, and Strauss all called Vienna home.

I surprised Sam with tickets to a Mozart concert in the Hofberg Hall – a posh venue with red velvet drapes, massive crystal chandeliers, and frescoed ceilings. There were ladies in chic formal dresses and men milling about in tuxedos.

We slinked in terribly underdressed, doing the best we could with the clothes we had in our bags. I was wearing a wrinkled black t-shirt with dirty black cycling tights that I pulled from the bottom of a pannier.

"Well, at least the dark colors hide the grease stains."

Sam's attire, a floral sundress with bike shoes, made me snicker.

She whispered in my ear, "Hey, did you know this was a black-tie event? I feel like everyone is looking at us."

"Maybe I did; maybe I didn't," I squirmed. "Don't worry, Honey, you look beautiful."

We laughed it off and enjoyed ourselves. For me, it was fun to stand out...for the same reason I enjoy wearing fake teeth into dive bars.

We spent the next day visiting Vienna's museums and palaces. Sam was excited to see Gustav Klimt's masterpiece, "The Kiss," at the Belvedere Palace, while I was more interested in the manicured gardens and hedge mazes at Schloss Schönbrunn.

Although the gelato cart vendor at the main entrance seemed like a nice guy, he was a horrible street performer. He'd scoop gelato into a cone, turn it upside down, and hold it there for thirty seconds. Whether it was the excessive heat that day or just poor execution, there was a pool of melted gelato on the asphalt below. He dropped two more scoops before finally handing Sam an intact cone.

We felt rested and recharged after three nights in a hotel. We decided to ship all the items we no longer needed to a depot in Munich for pick-up before our flight home. Since we'd be crossing the Alps soon, lightening our load by fifteen pounds would make it easier to pedal uphill, put less strain on the drivetrain, and open up pack space.

After our final Früstück in the hotel, consisting of assorted meats, cheeses, and breads, we climbed aboard Greeny and streaked like a bullet train for Slovakia.

☸ 🚶 ☉

Chapter 38
Steel Skies Over the Iron Curtain

From our vantage point on a sunny Austrian hillside, the gloomy flatlands surrounding Bratislava looked foreboding. Dark skies hung sinisterly over the communist blocs in the distance.

"So, are you ready to go behind the Iron Curtain?" I asked with trepidation in my voice.

"I guess so, but I'm not very excited about it. It doesn't look very impressive from here."

"Oh, come on," I said reassuringly, "it will be an adventure. Every country I've ever visited has had something to offer. How shitty can post-communism be?"

Answer: A shitload shittier.

Minutes later, we found ourselves staring down the barrel of a machine gun. Somehow we'd crossed the Slovakian border illegally and needed to go back to the border control station. The strapping young soldier lowered his gun and walked us back to Austria.

Once there, he instructed us to get on the motorway with all the other vehicles. Rolling up to a customs and immigration booth behind an automobile reminded us of the time we took Greeny through a fast food drive-thru in the Netherlands.

The immigration agent snatched our passports from my hands, looked at our tandem, and rolled his eyes in disdain. He begrudgingly stamped them and motioned for us to pass without saying a single word.

The narrow bike path that led to the city center was littered with debris. It had rusty barbwire fences on both sides, and there were unexpected dead ends that forced us to slam on the brakes and backtrack again and again. It was impossible to build any momentum.

"This bike path is more puzzling than the hedge maze at Schönbrunn," Sam kidded.

☼ ⚦ ⊙

Having ridden across bike-friendly countries thus far, we missed the safety and serenity of the well-developed cycling infrastructure of the Schengen area. We made our way through Bratislava's streets, dodging protruding rebar and rim-eating potholes. Eventually we reached the Altstadt, the picturesque historic zone that looks exactly like old Austria. The two countries must have been indistinguishable from one another before the communist sprawl.

Aside from that cheery part of town, we found a city of indifferent people that didn't seem to notice us. Trash blew through the empty streets of the bleak neighborhoods, giving them a post-apocalyptic feel.

"Once we're in the countryside, I'm sure it will get better," Sam said optimistically. "I mean, how depressing can cornfields be?"

"You're probably right, but there's something unnerving about this place. Often times, the poorest countries have the friendliest people. Not here though; there's no warmth at all."

Although we'd hoped to camp in the countryside, we were unsure about our security, so we decided to find a hotel. We rode around aimlessly looking for one before finally asking for directions.

Everyone we approached ignored us – as if we were ghosts they couldn't hear or see. We finally found a man who was willing to assist. Of the two hotels in town, he recommended the Capri – and pointed to it on our map.

The massive lobby at the Capri Hotel contained only one piece of furniture – a ratty old sofa. In the center of the blank white space was a reception desk in a box the size of a shipping container. There were two female ogres smoking cigarettes inside. The air in there looked toxic.

I approached one of them and asked, "We'd like a room for this evening, what's the price for a double?"

"Forty euros, you pay first," the mono-browed clerk replied.

I slid €40 and a completed registration card to her through the slit in the bullet-proof glass.

She slid it all back to me. "Not now. Busy. You wait," she said, pointing to the soiled sofa.

☼ 🏃 ◉

After forty minutes of being stretched out on the filthy carpet, because it looked cleaner than the sofa, I approached them again.

"Um. Just wondering how much longer it will be? We've been riding all day and would like to take a shower."

"Not now. Busy. You wait."

Several people had arrived after us; everyone was sitting around waiting for the office to open. When the clerk finally motioned for us to approach, two men tried to wrestle their way in front of us.

I blocked them with my forearms and shouted, "We were here first!"

Once I checked in, the clerk slid me a skeleton key and a plastic chit with a number engraved in it. I gathered our things and started walking the tandem toward the elevator.

"Stop!" the ogre screamed as she rushed after me. "Bicycle in back. Give man this," she said, holding up a chit like the one she'd given me.

I begged – to no avail – to bring the bike into our room.

"Bicycle in back!"

The ten-foot concrete wall encircling the hotel's parking lot was rimmed with razor wire. There were two guards, one in a watchtower and one patrolling the perimeter with a German Shepherd on a short leash. They wore Russian Ushanka hats and had machine guns strapped to their shoulders.

"Where the hell am I, Gulag 17?" I mumbled to myself.

They snatched the bike from me, attached a tag with my chit number on it, and ghost-rolled it into a metal shipping container – where it fell over with an indignant crash.

When I chased after Greeny to stand her upright and put a lock through the wheel, the guard grabbed my arm, denying me access, and pointed for me to leave.

Back in the hotel, Sam and I waited for the only elevator in the ten-story building – a wooden crate the size of a telephone booth with one missing door. Since it only held four lean adults, we knew we'd be waiting five or six trips based on our position in line.

☼ ⚲ ◉

The group of Chinese software engineers in front of us seemed content waiting, but I was getting impatient and started looking for a stairway – eventually concluding that there wasn't one.

I whispered to Sam, "Well, there wouldn't have been any way to get the tandem into that elevator even if we were allowed to bring it inside the room. Without stairs, I wonder what they do if the elevator breaks down."

"Don't even go there; this place already gives me the creeps."

The elevator stopped abruptly when it reached the fifth floor. We found our room at the end of a blank hallway. It was a concrete cube with two rock-hard beds and an orange Formica counter that ran down the length of one wall. There was a communal bathroom that lacked towels, soap, and toilet paper. Surely those items could be purchased at the reception desk – if you're willing to endure two elevator rides and a bout with two ogres.

There was only one knob on the sink and shower faucets because there was only one temperature of water – frickin' freezing. The view from the window was unimpressive, too: just empty gray streets and bloc housing. Most disturbingly, I didn't see a fire escape.

"This place is a death trap. If there's a fire, we're goners."

"Come on, Babe, we're only here for one night. Besides, we'll be back in our tent tomorrow…all alone in the countryside. That tent never sounded so good."

"I'm not so sure about stealth-camping in Slovakia, Sam. Based on the level of security in the parking lot, it may not be safe. We'd be sitting ducks if we got jumped in the middle of nowhere."

"If you're that worried about it, maybe we should bail on Budapest and head back to Austria."

"Let's give it a try tomorrow. If we're not having fun, we'll turn back. That's assuming, of course, that our bike is still there in the morning."

I stayed awake that night reflecting on how fortunate I was to have been born into a free and prosperous country with

☼ 🏃 ⊙

unlimited opportunities. Had I been born behind the Iron
Curtain, I probably wouldn't be where I was and doing
what I was doing.

After some wicked-cold showers the next day, we gathered our
bags and waited thirty minutes for an elevator ride to the lobby. During the
wait, we confirmed that there was no other way down. Once we reached
the ground floor we decided to have breakfast in the adjacent café.

"I'm starving," Sam said as she perused the coffee-stained menu.
"I'm getting the mushroom omelet. What about you?"

"I'm getting the toasted ham and cheese sandwich. Eat up, Sammi;
we've got a long day of riding ahead of us."

The waiter delivered pure disappointment. Sam's single-egg
omelet had a sliver of mushroom and cucumber in it, and my sandwich
barely had anything between the slices of stale bread.

"This omelet is terrible. It's cold and burnt; how the heck did they
do that?"

"My sandwich is awful too. It's bread-on-bread until you reach the
center."

Thankfully, our bike was still intact. After loading it, we rode
across a busy bridge that spanned the Danube in the direction of Hungary.
The wide shoulder was littered with debris, including a car bumper that
looked like it'd been there for awhile. To our dismay, there were drivers
intentionally swerving toward us. They'd honk and laugh at our terrified
expressions as they zoomed off.

We got off the thoroughfare and onto a frontage road that ran
along the south bank of the river. There were endless housing blocs on dirt
lots where the grass once grew. Laundry hung from every balcony.

In the distance, we saw five Slovakian soldiers with machine guns
shaking down cars traveling in both directions. After seeing them yank a
man from his car and draw guns on him, we stopped the bike to chat.

"Screw this, let's return to Austria. We'll have more fun in the
Alps and Tuscany than in the cornfields of Eastern Europe anyway. This is
supposed to be a vacation – so let's spend it somewhere fun."

☼ ⚲ ⊙

Sam wholeheartedly agreed, so we made an immediate about-face. Serendipitously, the skies cleared the moment we crossed back into Austria.

In a boisterous Biergarten a few hours later, we discussed our short-but-shitty ride around Bratislava.

"You know, although we interacted with dozens of people, not one person took any interest in us, our bike, or even our money. In my opinion, Bratislava is a blank slate."

Idealistic as always, Sam only had hope, "Well, now that Slovakia has joined the E.U. things are bound to get better. Hopefully, they'll have more freedom and wealth than they've had in generations. Let's toast to the happiness and prosperity of the Slovakian people."

We clinked our massive one-liter mugs and cheered, "Prost!"

Chapter 39
Alpenblow

The snowcapped mountains surrounding Innsbruck are always inspirational – even more so when they're gazed upon from the panoramic balcony of a boutique hotel at sunrise. It was a well-earned reward after so many nights of stealth-camping. Our rustic room had a feather bed, a thick down comforter, and handmade Tyrolean furniture. It felt fantastic to be fluffy.

"That was such a nice change," Sam said as we rode away. "I feel so refreshed."

"Me too; I haven't slept that well in months. Honey, if you want, we can stay another night."

"No, that's okay. I'd rather be alone in our tent on a mountaintop somewhere. I'm rested and ready to ride."

Sam's positive outlook, easygoing attitude, and thirst for adventure made her a delightful touring companion – and she seemed to enjoy the exercise as much as I did.

The ride up the Inn River towards Switzerland had some of the most majestic scenery we'd seen thus far. Reminiscent of Yosemite, the mile-wide valley floor is abutted by granite walls on either side. The lush hillsides are dotted with chalets with blooming geraniums under every window. Occasionally, we'd stop for a hearty meal in a picturesque village with a Tyrolean band playing.

The bike paths in the region are outstanding – freshly paved and smooth as glass. We turned left and headed up the Ötztal Valley, a steep box canyon in the direction of Italy. The peaks of the Ötztaller Alpen soared above us as we crept up their granite flanks.

After several grueling hours of climbing, we stopped for lunch at a Gasthof. We decided to get a room there after I started feeling ill.

A pharmacist at the nearby Apotheke prescribed some herbal teas and local honey – claiming that I'd feel better by morning. Apparently I was suffering from allergies to the abundant wildflowers – and the

☼ ⚡ ☉

concentrated pollen in the local honey was the tried-and-true mountain remedy.

"Thanks for taking care of me, Sammi; I feel much better today."

"I'm glad. That pharmacist knew exactly what to do."

"You know, I haven't been sick since I quit my job – even though I've been exposed to plenty of germs. Think about all the train stations, campgrounds, and restaurants we've been in."

"That's because you're not all stressed out and getting plenty of sleep and exercise."

"After knowing what it feels like to be happy, healthy, and free, I wonder if I'll ever be able to return to a normal life."

"Maybe think about it this way: cruising is your normal life. You've discovered that about yourself. You're a rolling stone, Honey, and that will never change. Even if you go home for a while, it's only a matter of time until you're back out there again. That's what cruisers do."

"I hope you're right, Sammi. I really hope you are."

The glistening Alps beckoned us to wander upon them. We stowed Greeny in a ski storage locker under the Gasthof and headed up the mountain with our daypacks. The mousey manager recommended we overnight in the summit hut rather than make the trip in a single day.

Indeed, the extensive network of huts throughout the Alps is a blessing to high-country wanderers – with warm food, cold beer, and inexpensive lodging just a few miles apart. It makes it possible, albeit not recommended, to travel across the highest mountains in Europe without a tent, sleeping bag, or even much food.

We reached the stone hut in the early afternoon. Perched on the precipice of a protruding ledge, the chalet overlooked the emerald-green valley below. It had red and white chevron-striped shutters, the colors of the Austrian flag, and there was a Ratskeller tavern bored into the rock below. We could hear yodeling emanating from the back deck and echoing down the valley walls.

Two ladies were entertaining a lively crowd there, one on an accordion and the other on a guitar. Everyone locked arms, clinked mugs, and sang along.

✿ 🎿 ◉

The musicians took a liking to us, smiling in our direction as they sang. During one of their frequent "wine breaks," they approached us with a great deal of curiosity. Before they began playing again, they recounted our journey to the audience with amazing accuracy and toasted to our open-ended plans for the future. They dedicated some American ballads to us, like "She'll Be Coming Round the Mountain" and "Bring Back My Bonnie" – with an improvised yodel here and there.

We checked into the hut and were given the keys to a bedroom on the upper floor with an unobstructed view of the valley several thousand feet below. Each of the rooms had six pinewood bunks, three on each side. We felt fortunate to have the room to ourselves since all of the other rooms were fully occupied. There wasn't much privacy, though. We could hear every word our Scottish neighbors were saying through the plywood partition left open at the top.

For dinner, we both ordered Käsespätzle, a traditional baked noodle and cheese dish that's a local specialty. Although this Germanic version of mac and cheese is delicious, we learned the hard way that it can be highly volatile at high altitudes – producing flatulence of unimaginable proportions.

"It might be a good idea to put in earplugs tonight. If my snoring doesn't keep you awake, my farts probably will," I said as I climbed into the bottom bunk across the aisle from Sam.

Suddenly, it became serious. No matter how hard I clinched, I couldn't hold back a blast that rattled the windows and charred the bedpost. Sam belted off some impressive ones, too, before we turned to each other, across the aisle, and simultaneously concluded:

"Käsespätzle!"

Sleep was impossible. For the rest of the night, there was an eruption every three minutes. Even after Sam drifted off to sleep, she kept rattling off dainty ones. I snickered with satisfaction when one of mine woke her up.

We overheard our Scottish neighbors the next morning.

☼　☂　☉

"I can't believe it went on all bloody night," a man complained.

A lady replied, "It was an awful scent."

Upon hearing that, Sam and I both burst into laughter. Our neighbors undoubtedly heard us giggling, but we couldn't contain it. As luck would have it, we were seated across from them at breakfast. Uncharacteristic of Scots, they weren't friendly at all. To them, we were terrorists.

Although it was embarrassing at the time, it became an endearing memory.

"It was an awful scent," Sam giggled sometime later. "I still can't believe that lady actually said that. Let's agree to never order that entree on mountaintops again."

Chapter 40
The Great Italian Downhill

If you ever find yourself crossing the Tyrolean Alps on a bicycle, you'll be rewarded with a thrilling downhill into Italy that lasts all day. Careening down the twisting turns, we tucked-in tightly to go even faster. Some pitches were so steep that, had we not had a drag-brake, surely we would have sped out of control.

"Now that we're in Italy, I want pizza," Sam insisted.

"I'm not so sure about that. After that whole Alpenblow ordeal, I may never eat cheese again. I saw a side of myself that I hope to never see again."

"Look, Buster, I've always wanted to come to Italy, and now that I'm finally here, I want pizza. Keep your eyes peeled for a pizzeria."

Not having any success finding one, we stopped and asked some locals for help. They directed us to a restaurant in a fourteenth-century castle overlooking the Isarco River.

Upon finding it, we were seated at a marble table in a grassy courtyard with the sound of cascading whitewater in the background. We paired the pies with Chianti and topped them off with tiramisu. Italy felt like a major milestone in our journey – a whole new world of cuisine and cultural fascination.

"Hey Sammi, on the back of the menu it says this place is also a hotel. Would my lady fancy a chamber in the castle this evening?" I said in a regal tone.

"Indeed, fine, sir," she said, holding out her hand for me to kiss. "¿Por qué no?"

After dinner, we were shown to our room up the dizzying spiral staircase by the proprietor, named Anna. There were suits of armor in the alcoves of each landing, with tapestries depicting various aspects of castle life adorning the walls.

☼ ⚲ ☉

We were excited to be shown the prized suite atop the highest tower. It had a conical roof supported by irregular timbers that had obviously stood the test of time.

As I was dozing off, I thought about all the people who slept there before us – and wondered how many of them were now restless spirits roaming the castle at night.

The following morning, Anna brought out a bountiful breakfast with a large assortment of fresh fruit. We lavished her with compliments for the truly outstanding stay before departing.

"Just curious," I asked, "are there any ghosts in this castle?"

"Yes, many," she said with great certainty. "All the castles in Italy have ghosts. Thankfully, all of ours are friendly...well, except for one."

The air thickened as we descended the widening valley that turned deciduous as the terrain moderated. The flowery bike path was tunneled through a sea of fruit orchards on either side.

Occasionally, we'd catch a glimpse of a granite peak towering above the red-roofed villas in the distance. The greenness of the grass, the blueness of the sky, and the whiteness of the clouds made the setting seem surreal.

In Trento, we checked into a stylish pension with a padded leather door. Sam was craving pasta – and needed to eat before she bonked. I've learned to never ignore a hungry stoker, for they're an unpredictable lot even on a full stomach. After perusing the menu for pasta, she predictably ordered pizza.

Per the advice of some locals, we veered west and climbed back into the mountains toward Riva del Garda, a popular place for cycling. Indeed it was, there were numerous riders on the road and congregated around the marble fountains in the village squares.

As we crested the summit, after a grueling climb, we were greeted with a breathtaking view of Lago Garda, or "Guardian Lake." The long sapphire lake, rimmed with decomposed white marble beaches, is unmistakably Italian. The lavish columned estates had fountains, statues, and gazebos terraced down the rocky outcroppings to the water's edge.

"I'm pretty sure this is what heaven looks like," Sam sighed. "At least my version of it."

Overlooking Riva del Garda

We pulled into a campground on the eastern shore and pitched the tent in a prime location with an unobstructed view of the mountains, lake, and beach below us.

Although the campground was remarkably well situated, it had grimy bathrooms that were missing toilet seats. There wasn't any toilet paper either – however it could be purchased in the ratty campground store for an outrageous price.

The coin-operated showers were straight from hell. The expensive tokens barely got the water lukewarm for a stingy amount of time before blasting you with cold water the moment the time expired. We witnessed countless unhappy campers complaining in loud voices to the apathetic staff. I'd wager that a sizable chunk of the campground's annual revenue comes from dripping wet campers, with shampoo still in their hair, trying to buy another token before they freeze to death.

☼ ⚲ ☉

The campground was worth staying at, though. We swam in the cool, clear lake and relaxed our tired bodies in the sun. We befriended the couple camped next to us, Andre and Sophie. They were fascinated by our adventure.

He was a chiseled firefighter that enjoyed carving wood furniture, and she was a slender brunette schoolteacher with striking blue eyes. They invited us to accompany them to dinner one evening and drove us there in their car.

The following day, the four of us spent the morning on the beach and the afternoon tramping around the historic town of Malcesine. The city center was plastered with posters for Gardaland – a nearby theme park that claimed to be Italy's largest and most popular.

"It's better than Disney," our waitress exaggerated. "My son and daughter used to work there every summer, so I should know."

It sounded like a fun diversion, and we needed a rest from riding. Feeling run-down from overtraining, a day at a theme park would give our cramping muscles a well-earned break.

Sam and I sang from the patio of a trattoria overlooking the lake, "We're going to Gardaland, we're going to Gardaland…"

Chapter 41
Gardaland

The next morning we packed our tent, loaded Greeny, and bid farewell to our newfound friends. Gardaland beckoned – just thirty miles down the barrel of the rifle-shaped lake.

The terrain flattened and the temperature rose as we pushed south toward the rolling plains of the Regione Veneto. It became so congested with cars and pedestrians that it took most of the day to ride the short distance. The beaches were so packed with bare breasts that there wasn't room for another pair.

We were correct in our assumption that there'd be plenty of campgrounds around Gardaland. We found dozens – with amenities ranging from loud-and-crowded to loud-and-crowded-with-a-pool.

"Why is it so busy on a Sunday?" I asked the campground clerk at the least offensive one.

"It's a summer holiday in Italy; this is our busiest week of the year."

As I stepped out of the office, I saw something that would summarize our stay: a little boy was peeing into a pool packed with screaming children.

"Mama Mia! So much for going swimming. For every one you see, there are probably fifty more you don't."

"Well, at least there's a lake to swim in," Sam reminded me.

We pitched a tent between two campervans and spent the remainder of the day stretched-out on the lush lawn reading. That evening, we walked to a lakefront sports bar to watch the 2004 Summer Olympics. It was packed with fans watching a soccer match that Italy was playing in.

Suddenly, there was a loud commotion outside. Everyone in the bar rushed out to see what was going on. There was a stocky drunk man with curly black hair making a complete ass out of himself after receiving a parking ticket. He was shoving the police officers back and screaming at them. Each time he pushed them, the crowd oohed and awed.

☼ ⚲ ◉

The officers spoke casually among themselves as they were being assaulted; then one turned his back to the assailant to call headquarters on his flip-phone. We couldn't believe what we were seeing. We expected to see the perpetrator handcuffed and hauled off. Instead, the fancy-pants cops in white patent leather loafers sulked shamefully into the shadows – pretending not to hear the insults being hurled at them from the crowd.

"Those cops are so passive," I pronounced. "Too much posing and not enough policing, if you ask me."

The next morning we stood at the gates of Gardaland, waiting for them to open at the far end of the cobblestone piazza. A statue of Prezzemolo, a green dragon with red hair and floppy yellow ears, rotated in the center fountain. The adoring Italian children wore embroidered beanies with floppy ears in lieu of mouse ears on their heads.

We felt claustrophobic as the crowd compressed upon us, shoulder-to-shoulder in a sea of sweaty Italians in tank tops. As the opening trumpets began trumpeting, teenage boys literally climbed over the crowd, stepping on shoulders and balancing on heads, in an effort to be the first ones through the gate.

We underestimated the size and scope of Gardaland – it was much more expansive than anticipated and had a Disneyesque attention to detail, with similarly themed attractions.

"This amusement park was pretty amusing," I said as we sat on a park bench watching the electric light parade at the end of the day. "I've decided animatronics are even cheesier when they speak Italian."

"Yeah, this place was better than I thought it would be," Sam said as she dunked chocolate-drizzled cookies into her cappuccino. "Grazie, Gardaland."

☼   🕴   ◉

Chapter 42
Tears of Joy in a Floating City

The next day we bid "ciao" to our campground and pedaled down the country road adjacent to it. We spun through the undulating fields toward Venice, making Verona, the fabled home of Romeo and Juliet, by midday.

Without the comfort and safety of a bike path, we decided to take back-roads through the farmland. Unfortunately, every one was riddled with congested traffic, self-centered drivers, and semi-trucks.

"Welcome to summertime in Italy," I whined. "Maybe the Italian couple we met on the Danube were right; maybe we are gonna die-a."

A major downside to bikepacking through a country that's overrun by tourists every summer is that stealth-camping is illegal. In Italy, camping is only permitted in designated campgrounds – otherwise, everyone would do it.

Even though the locals warned us that we'd be arrested for trespassing and taken to jail if we camped illegally, we were faced with a dilemma outside of Lonigo – whether to ride until we found a campground or duck into a hidden place and take our chances with the police. After a near-miss by a big truck, we decided it was getting too dark to continue. We pulled into a rolling vineyard for the night.

"It's a perfect place to pitch a tent," I proclaimed. "It's level and grassy between the rows of grapes – and well hidden from the road. Besides, if the cops try to arrest us, I'll just push them around until they walk away."

"What if the sprinklers come on in the middle of the night?"

"The grapes are close to being harvested. I doubt they'll put any water on them at this stage, and I don't see any irrigation pipes for root watering."

We leaned the tandem against a large oak and started unpacking it. Sam spotted a farmhouse through the hanging grapes, with an elderly gentleman outside tending to his vegetable garden. He wore tan corduroy pants, a brown woolen coat, and a black beret. Judging from his hunched posture, he was probably in his nineties.

As awkward as it was, I walked up to him and humbly asked if we could camp in his vineyard overnight – promising to be gone first thing in the morning. He looked at me with his smiling brown eyes and gestured for us to camp anywhere we liked. Without saying a word, his kindheartedness rang clear.

He was everyone's grandfather…

That evening, I thought about the old man as I looked up at the stars through the tent's mesh ceiling. I wondered what he'd seen in his lifetime of living in central Europe. He was probably just a boy during World War I and perhaps a soldier in World War II. A product of harsher times, he'd undoubtedly survived war and strife. I envisioned Roman soldiers fighting in the fields around us and wondered how many weary travelers had camped there before us.

We reached Camping Fusina the following day – a massive complex across a muddy bay from Venice. Since bicycles and cars are not allowed in the city, it was as close as we could get on Greeny. We picked a comfortable campsite under a shady willow tree and read in the afternoon sun.

That evening we took the ferry into Venice, one of the best walking cities in the world – especially on a sultry summer night like the one we were having. With its twisted canals, countless bridges, and secret alleyways, there's a surprise around every corner. Ornate cathedrals, grand piazzas, and outdoor eateries seem to pop up when you least expect it.

I'd visited Venice once in my early twenties, when I made the tragic mistake of going there alone. It was painful to see all the young lovers kissing on the bridges. It seemed

*like everyone had someone except me. I fled the city and
vowed never to return without a loved one by my side.*

The romantic setting moved Sam. At a quiet restaurant at the end
of an alley, tears began to flow.

"This is one of the most beautiful places I've ever been," she
sniffled. "Thank you so much for bringing me here."

"I'm lucky to be here with you, Sammi, and you brought yourself
here. Perhaps more than anyone else in this city, you brought yourself –
and you've got the chiseled legs to prove it."

After a multicourse meal, we left the restaurant and walked around
holding hands.

"The last ferry to Fusina leaves in ninety minutes – and we need to
be on it. It's a quick trip by boat, but a long distance by train or bus. Let's
start heading back toward the ferry dock. This town is so confusing that it
could take awhile to find it. The next time we come, I'm bringing the
GPS."

Sam concurred. "Even a compass would be helpful… At least
we'd know that we're headed in the right direction. It's too cloudy to
navigate by the stars, but don't worry, we've got plenty of time to figure it
out."

Desperately disoriented, I bought a city map from an information
kiosk that unfortunately didn't have street names on it; only points of
interest and major canals were marked on this condensed version. Still, I
figured with a map we could ask locals to point out our current location –
to make sure we were headed in the right direction.

With fifty minutes remaining, we were becoming frazzled. Yet
another store clerk informed us that we had walked in the wrong direction.
We were now further away than we were at dinner.

We changed our strategy and tried to follow the easily identifiable
Gran Canal as it looped around the city. It wasn't easy, though; dead ends
had us backtracking again and again, and before long we were completely
lost in the city's concentric rings. We came upon places we'd already been,

☼ ⚲ ◉

obviously going in circles. With only thirty minutes to spare, we started sprinting.

"This place is crazy," I moaned. "We need to get a position fix every couple of minutes so we don't get off track."

We kept getting conflicting information. One person would put us in the middle of the map, and minutes later another person would place us miles away. It was obvious that Venetians are as confused by the city's cartography as the tourists.

With only twenty minutes left, we stumbled upon the only bus station and located it on the map. It couldn't have been further away from the ferry dock and still be within city limits. In a last ditch effort, we hailed a water taxi, something we should have tried sooner, but were told that it was impossible to reach the ferry in time.

How could this happen? After navigating the poorly charted waters of Mexico and negotiating our way through countless European cities, we found ourselves unable to escape the clutches of Venice – even with a map, ample time, and local assistance.

Thankfully, there was one last bus to Fusina after a transfer in Mestre. In retrospect, finding the bus station was a blessing in disguise. Had we been looking for it, we surely wouldn't have found it.

We instantly regretted returning to the campground. Dozens of party tour buses had arrived, and a sea of red pup tents were stretched out across the lawn. The bar was overflowing with rowdy Australians on a drunken walkabout. As topless girls danced on tables, their punchy boyfriends wrestled in the mud below.

Sam covered her eyes and walked away after two guys head-butted each other so hard it caused their foreheads to split open. The crowd cheered as the blood began to flow. We went back to the tent, climbed into our sleeping bags, put in earplugs, and tried to ignore the thumping techno beat that went on all night.

☼ 🕴 ◉

We returned to Venice the following day – this time with our handheld GPS. Navigating the city became infinitely less difficult with an instrument to guide us.

"Have you noticed that all the stores are selling the exact same souvenirs? It's worse than Fisherman's Wharf."

Sam giggled, "Yeah, if you're not looking for a glass figurine or masquerade mask, you're pretty much out of luck."

We bought slices of pizza from a take-away window at a restaurant and sat down on the curb to eat them. A portly waiter motioned for us to sit at an outdoor table.

"Thank you, but we're fine here."

"Please sit," he insisted, pulling out a chair. "It will be much more comfortable for you."

Feeling that it would be rude to decline his generosity, we collected our things and moved to the table.

"That was really nice," Sam said sweetly, "but I didn't mind the curb."

After we finished eating, we left a generous tip and got up to leave.

"Stop!" someone shouted.

It was our waiter. He ran to our table, holding a dinner check in his hand. Confused, because we'd already paid for the meal, I turned it over. It read: "coperto," a table service fee in Italy.

"Surely there's a mistake; you practically insisted we sit here. Besides, the coperto is twice the price of our meal – and you didn't even serve us."

"You sat at my table; you pay coperto or I'll call the police."

"You've got to be kidding. Your restaurant is practically empty, we didn't use any utensils, and we left a big tip."

"Pay coperto or I'm calling the police."

"Okay, okay," I conceded. Then I turned to Sam and whispered, "Get ready to run."

Sensing our tenacity, he hovered over us like a vulture, waiting for me to pay. I pulled out my wallet and began awkwardly fumbling with it in an effort to buy time. The moment he stepped inside to attend to another

☼   ⚕   ☉

table, we grabbed the tip and dashed. I knew it would be impossible for a man of his stature to catch us in the hordes of people and mazelike streets. When we found open space, we broke away – running like we'd just committed a gem heist.

"What a scam," Sam said after we were in the clear. "I've never dined-and-dashed before, but in that situation it was the right thing to do."

"It was extortion. Technically speaking, we didn't dine-and-dash, though, because we paid for our meal. It was more of a sit-and-dash offense."

Chapter 43
Under The Tuscan Bush

Florence is perpetually bustling with tourists and street vendors in the summertime. Although this is one of Europe's most beautiful cities, steeped in Renaissance charm, it's also one of the biggest tourist traps. After a disappointing stay in a dilapidated hotel and several mediocre meals, we longed for the peace and serenity of the countryside.

"I'm glad we're skipping the museums," Sam said as we rode out of town. "They'd be way too crowded to enjoy anyway."

Unlike our typical strategy of following great rivers, our tour through the hills of Tuscany would consist of countless climbs and glorious descents. Although the scenery was captivating, the sweltering temperatures and windless canyons had us seeking shelter from the sun. At times, it felt unbearable.

We stopped for gelato at a tiny market in a densely wooded ravine. Two Italian cops sat at the lunch counter, sipping cappuccinos and watching auto racing. They wore tight baby-blue uniforms and had patent white leather shoes, belts, and gun holsters.

I whispered to Sam, "How can you fight crime dressed like that?"

"They must be the fashion police," she responded. "I've heard about them."

We both started laughing. They looked back at us.
They knew we were talking about them...

The cultivated hillcrests around Chianti are quintessentially Tuscan – each with a stone winery atop it. After a long climb up a high pass, we stopped just before the summit for a picture of the pastoral backdrop before our highly anticipated descent into Siena at sunset.

Then tragedy struck...

⚓ 🚴 ☀

As we straddled the bike to finish the climb, we allowed it to roll backwards momentarily before standing on the pedals. There was a snapping sound as the torsion from the opposing forces sheared the rear axle – causing the frame to sink lamely to the ground.

"Oh, that's just great," I grumbled, "of all the spare parts we've been lugging around, I can't find our spare rear axle. Either we lost it or I accidentally shipped it to Munich with the rest of our stuff."

"Getting another one shouldn't be a big deal, right? I'm sure there are plenty of bike shops in Italy."

"I would assume so, but tandem axles can be tricky to find because they're longer than regular ones to accommodate the drum brake. Without a rear axle, we can't even walk it down."

Stranded atop a mountain in a remote part of Italy, we evaluated our predicament and searched for a temporary fix. Nothing was evident.

We had no other choice but to seek help, so we stood next to the broken-down bike with our thumbs out. Before long, an SUV stopped. The driver rolled down his passenger-side window to speak with us.

"Is there a problem with your bike?" he asked in perfect English.

"Yes, the axle sheared, and we need to find a bicycle shop to fix it. Do you know of any around here?"

"There aren't any in Castellina, but there's a machine shop there that may be able to fabricate a new one or weld the old one back together. Unfortunately, they've closed for the day – so you'll have to wait until the morning. I'm heading into Castellina now if you want a ride. Would you like me to call a nearby hotel and check their availability?"

"Yes, please, that would be great," Sam and I simultaneously responded.

After reserving us a room, he walked to the rear of his vehicle and dropped the tailgate. We shook hands.

"My name is Tobias. You can load your things in here."

Not sure whether we could trust him or not, I envisioned him jumping in the car and driving off with our luggage. It wouldn't have been a total loss though because I learned to keep my valuables in a secret compartment under my clothes after being assaulted by gypsy kids outside the Roman Colosseum a few years back.

> *A college buddy and I stashed our backpacks in lockers and went out to tour Rome with our valuables in fanny packs around our waists.*
>
> *Outside the Colosseum, we were rushed by a mob of children. Thinking they were innocent beggars, he allowed them to encircle him. As soon as they did, they placed pieces of cardboard around his waist that prevented him from reaching his pockets.*
>
> *They swarmed like piranhas, picked him clean, and scattered in every direction. This brawny college football linebacker lost everything, including his passport, money, and airline tickets. Thankfully, I managed to hold the horde off by taking a defensive posture when they came for me.*

When I started to load Greeny in Tobias' car, he stopped me and said, "Sorry, friend, but I can't take the bike – it's just too big and greasy. You'll have to leave it here and come back for it later."

With darkness less than an hour away and very little food and water, we had no choice but to abandon it. I removed the broken wheel, so we could bring it with us to repair, and pushed the rest of the bike deep into the thick vegetation.

Once it was hidden from the road, I locked it to a pine tree and wrestled my way out of the bushes. I brushed off the needles and leaves, got in the car, and marked the location on the GPS. The last thing we needed was another navigational fiasco like we had in Venice.

"There's no way I'm losing that bike under a Tuscan bush. I just hope no one else finds it before we return."

"Are you serious? There's no way anyone will ever find that bike in those bushes," Sam scoffed. "After all, it's green."

☼ 🚶 ◉

"And even if they do, it's only got one wheel," Tobias added. "Who's going to steal a bike with one wheel?"

As a renowned viticulture hydrologist with a consulting firm in the region, Tobias prepared water and soil reports for wine growers all around the world. By all accounts, he was very successful at it. He spoke passionately about his vocation, especially when he described Tuscany.

"There's no place in the world with as much soil diversity as here. The exact same seeds planted on those two hills," he said, pointing to them, "will produce completely different wines."

Apparently, the tremendous variation of sun, soil, and hydrological conditions within a small area accounts for the wide range of varietals grown there.

He drove us by the machine shop in Castellina in Chianti, so we'd know where it was, and dropped us off at the boutique hotel in the center of the hilltop village. We offered to buy him dinner, but he declined, saying that he had a report to finish that evening.

After freshening up, Sam and I wandered through the charming streets of the tiny town full of shops and restaurants. It's a setting that could only exist in Italy, epitomizing the beauty of a country so adored by the rest of the world. We sipped full-bodied Chiantis and enjoyed the outstanding local cuisine at a restaurant with an outdoor terrace overlooking a verdant valley.

"Although it sucks to be stranded, we certainly could have broken down in worse places. Someday, I'll probably forget about the broken axle – but I'll never forget this evening."

"Me neither, Sammi. Being here with you is what Italy is all about."

After dinner, we wandered around the village, stopping for a kiss now and then under the arched loggias. It was a stunning night, and Sam is a stunning woman.

We took our broken wheel to the machine shop after breakfast the next morning, but I wasn't very optimistic about the outcome.

"I doubt they'll be able to fabricate a new bike axle because it has reverse threads on one side so the nuts won't loosen as the wheel spins," I said as we walked there, "but we'll see."

Sure enough, the machinist explained that it was impossible to weld the broken axle, and they didn't have the metal stock or reverse taps to make a new one. So we headed back to the hotel and asked the nice lady at the front desk to call a bike shop in Siena and explain the situation for us.

A few minutes later, a mechanic named Mario picked us up in a large white van. He drove us up the mountain to recover our beloved bike from the bushes.

By midday, we had it on a stand in his shop. Unfortunately, every axle in his inventory was much too short. Nothing would span the wide frame. Mario called every bike shop in the area looking for one.

They all had the same response: "We don't carry tandem parts and don't know anyone that does."

"It's impossible," Mario fussed as he rummaged through his box of axles. "I've never seen anything that long."

The bleakness of the situation began to sink in. Mario thought for a moment, and then said, "I have an idea; please follow me."

He led us to a subterranean cellar and opened the creaky door. The flimsy stairs led to a dank basement full of rusty bicycle parts. Unfortunately, after searching the underground junkyard for over an hour, we decided to give up. It seemed hopeless.

As we were ascending the stairs, I caught a glimpse of an axle-shaped object under bits of rubble in an otherwise empty corner of the cellar. Although it would surely be too short, just like all the others, there was a renewed sense of hope. Mario and Sam watched as I sifted through the debris, and then, like Arthur extracting Excalibur from the stone, I pulled out a tandem axle.

Mario made the sign of the cross on his chest and said, "It's a miracle. I've never had a tandem in my shop before and have no idea where it could have come from. And look, it's brand new; there's not one bit of rust on it. I'm telling you, it's a miracle."

Chills ran down my back…
It was the only place we hadn't looked.

Sam started dancing around. Mario was excited too, albeit spooked by the serendipity.

Since Greeny wouldn't be repaired until the following day, he gave us a ride to a hilly campground on the edge of town and promised to pick us up the next morning. It was a beautiful facility with rolling grassy hills, a large pool, and a snack bar. The warty-nosed witch in the cashier's booth, however, was mean as a snake. When she presented me with a €40.01 bill, I handed her forty euros in cash.

"I hope that's close enough. All my change is in the bottom of my bags, and they're already packed."

She snatched up the money with her bony fingers and sneered, "Where's my penny? Everyone's always taking my pennies and never giving me pennies. If you don't give me my penny, I'll call the police."

Annoyed by her overreaction, I plopped my panniers on the counter and dumped my dirty clothes out in front of her. The sweaty cycling garments smelled rank after spending several sweltering days in the bag. When I finally found a penny at the bottom, I placed it on the counter in front of her.

As I was repacking, I saw Mario's van pull up out of the corner of my eye. Seeing my escape vehicle, I left a pair of my stinkiest underwear on the counter and jumped in the van before she could cast a spell. The witch picked them up and started shouting something in Italian while her colleague laughed in the background.

Sam hid her face in her hands and said, "Oh, come on, did you really have to do that?"

"Absolutely I did. Grouchy would be proud."

Back at Mario's shop, Greeny was ready to ride. After everything he'd done, he presented us with a bill that was uncomfortably low. The transportation costs alone were worth more than what he was charging us, but he refused to accept another penny due to divine intervention.

☼   🏃   ◉

"God fixed that bike, not me."

Thrilled to be back on the road again, we pedaled in the direction of Rome. It didn't take long for the congested roads and inconsiderate drivers to have us rethinking our plans, though – so we stopped to discuss them.

"You know what? I'm tired of riding in Italy. It's a beautiful country with warm people, but it's just too adored by the rest of the world in the summer. I miss riding on designated bike paths and stealth camping by rivers."

Sam agreed, "Yeah, I'm sure the off-season is much better – and it wouldn't be so unbearably hot. Let's head to Switzerland, then. Although I'm sure Rome would be amazing, I'd rather be in the mountains than in some big city. Besides, we've got to head back north eventually to make it to Oktoberfest."

"Switzerland it is then, but let's take a train. The sooner we get there, the longer we'll have to enjoy it."

With that decision made, we rode to the Siena Train Station and caught a train to the rooftop of Europe.

☼ 🚶 ☉

Chapter 44
Swiss Bliss

T he radiant sunshine beamed down on our tent in a meadow full of
        alpine wildflowers. The heavy dew made the grass glisten all
        around us. Off in the distance, above the great glacial valley, stood
Mont Blanc, the tallest mountain in Europe, conically white against the
powder blue sky. It was a perfect summer's day.

Arriving late the night before, we hastily set up camp on a grassy
knoll just above the Oberwald Hauptbahnhof train station. At an altitude of
4,481 feet, it's one of the highest railway stations in Europe that's serviced
by cogless trains. Although it was still early in the morning, there was
activity inside, so I slid down the slippery slope in search of breakfast.

In Switzerland, everything is dear. Hiking back to our camp, I
cringed as I converted the cost of our breakfast into U.S. dollars.

Welcome to Switzerland...
stay as long as you can afford to.

After a few hours of reading in the sunshine, waiting for the tent to
dry, we hopped on the gravel bike path next to a babbling brook.

"That little creek is the mighty Rhône River," Sam said as she
looked at a map. "It flows through some of France's finest wine regions
before reaching the Mediterranean Sea."

The serene alpine villages were cathartic. The cool green valleys
rimmed with snowy glacial horns were a welcome change from the heat
and hustle of Italy. At times, Switzerland seems like God's personal train
set – with lush mountains as tunneled as the cheese.

Life couldn't have been easier. We poached swims in hotel pools
every afternoon and stealth-camped on the riverbanks on our way west in
the direction of Lake Geneva.

We came upon a campground at a hot spring and made the wise
decision to stay. Situated at the base of a mountain, it had massive indoor

and outdoor pools, polished-granite waterslides carved in the face of the rock, and diving platforms perched atop thirty-foot boulders.

Most of the campsites had spotless caravans parked in them, covered in Swiss flags. It seemed everyone was trying to "out-Swiss" their neighbor. I watched one lady clip the grass around her flower boxes and garden gnomes.

"I've never seen anyone mow their campsite before. She's been working on it for over an hour."

"Did you see the camper next to the bathroom? They had lace linens, crystal glasses, and formal china on their fold-out table. Talk about glamping…"

After a rejuvenating stay, we continued down the valley next to the ever-widening river. Since the restaurants were prohibitively expensive, especially at dinner, we usually bought a rotisserie chicken from a food truck before stopping for the evening. We enjoyed splurging on lunch, but kept breakfast and dinner simple.

"Switzerland has unsurpassed Alpine scenery, but it's almost too expensive to enjoy."

Sam concurred. "The quality of everything is outstanding, but it makes San Francisco seem cheap. Should we give our wallets a break and head to France?"

"Great idea, Sammi. We'll be traveling back through Switzerland on our way to Munich anyway. Why not see another beautiful country, especially if it's more affordable?"

☼ ⚲ ◉

Chapter 45
Fondue Rendezvous

I n the shadow of Mt. Blanc, the village of Chamonix sports one of Europe's premier ski resorts. Its off-piste chutes have attracted some of the world's foremost extreme skiers, including Scot Schmidt, who conquered the couloirs of the Aguille D'midi that were previously considered unskiable in Greg Stump's 1985 film, *"Blizzard of AAHS."*

Like many places in France, the village is an epicurean delight, with haute cuisine everywhere – even in the campgrounds. At a picturesque one east of town, we could even order fresh baguettes to be delivered to our tent each morning – still warm from the oven.

It was one of the most strikingly beautiful campgrounds we'd stayed at, with gothic black rock spires to the east and Mt. Blanc's snowy white peak to the southwest. The high glaciers there stay lit for several hours after the valley shadows. There's nothing quite like the Alpenglow of the western French Alps.

We spent most days hiking in the high country and evenings in the city center, enjoying the resort atmosphere and free outdoor entertainment. With our packs off the bike, we dashed around town with such speed and agility that we rode Greeny around just for fun.

We were thrilled to find a Mexican restaurant there. We'd been craving it for months. Pairing a chef from Guadalajara, produce from France, and chocolate from Switzerland produced one of the best molés I'd ever had. And the restaurants in France were refreshingly inexpensive.

At dinner one night, I brought up our travel plans as we dined on cheese fondue. "We should probably start heading north tomorrow, autumn is just around the corner."

"Oh my gosh, this is delicious."

"It's starting to get colder, the days are getting shorter, and Oktoberfest is only a few weeks away…"

"Try dipping the sausage and brown bread together; it's so yummy."

"Have you even heard a word I've said? What do you think? Should we start heading north tomorrow?"

"Only if there's cheese fondue there, because I'm not leaving if there isn't."

> *A few years later, I returned to France with Slasher and another friend to ride our own grueling version of the Tour de France that finished in front of the Arc de Triomphe. To make the finish line pictures look authentic, we hired two Australian girls, eating at a nearby café, to stand next to us and clap while we held up bouquets of flowers. We took turns wearing the yellow jersey and swapped positions on the podium so we could all appear as winners.*

Sam and I were bombing down the Napoleon Road beside the Arve River by daybreak. Commissioned by the undersized emperor in 1860, the carriage route between Geneva and Chamonix spawned development and prosperity throughout the region. We pedaled through the Piedmont all day until we reached the shores of Lake Geneva in the late afternoon.

Geneva is one of the most cosmopolitan and culturally diverse cities in the world. Embassies, financial institutions, and fine watchmakers adorn the commercialized southern shoreline.

If Geneva is a symbol of peace, then the prestigious north shore is certainly one of prosperity. The mansions with private beaches are hidden behind high walls and mechanized entry gates. Luckily, we found a campground on the lake just before sundown. Although we'd ridden well over a hundred miles and were famished, due to the exorbitant cost, we decided to share a steak. Sam gazed out on the moonlit lake from our outdoor table at the end of a dock.

"It feels like we're back aboard Marylee again. I sure miss our life on the water; it seems like a lifetime ago."

☼ ⚲ ◉

Chapter 46
The Ultimate Campsite

erched on a granite cliff overlooking the Lauterbrunnen Valley, the village of Mürren endures. Having been declared an avalanche zone by the Swiss Government, it remains uniquely rustic due to the fact that no new buildings are permitted.

There's a high-speed gondola running through town that whisks passengers from the valley floor to a mid-station in Mürren before continuing up the top of the Shilthorn. On its peak there's a rotating metallic restaurant, the "Piz Gloria," immortalized as the ultramodern lair of supervillain Blofeld in the 1969 James Bond film, *"On Her Majesty's Secret Service."* The extravagant design is a striking reminder that you're in one of the richest and most advanced countries in the world.

Rather than taking the gondola, we chose to ride up the gravel access road from the valley floor. Upon reaching the village, we purchased groceries at a small market and hiked the bike up a grassy hillside in search of a place to camp. In a clearing deep inside the dense forest, we found perfection.

The campsite had running water, a carved rock sink, a wooden picnic bench, a large stone fireplace, and a woodshed with a sign on it that read: "Free Firewood, Please Help Yourself" written in English.

"This is the most incredible campsite I've ever seen. If it had showers and a TV, it would be a luxurious hotel."

Sam agreed, "It's the most beautiful place we've camped, that's for sure."

"Don't you think it's funny that our favorite anchorage and favorite campsite are the antithesis of one another? I mean, one's a cactus-lined cove in chaotic Mexico, and the other is a snowcapped peak in precise Switzerland. Can you get any more opposite than that?"

Across the tremendous valley, the region's highest peak, Jungfrau, had billowy white clouds clinging to its flanks. Waterfalls rushed down the rock face and vanished into the misty forest below.

☼ 🏃 ◉

The clear blue skies and crisp mountain air inspired us to hike above the tree line the next morning. We stopped at a mountain hut for goulash soup, ice cream, and beer before returning to our campsite just as the sun started setting.

Just then, my satellite phone rang. It was Tim informing me that my niece, Alora, had just been born. Whenever I reminisce about that place, I always think of her.

> *She's all grown up now – and she's a wonderful writer.*
> *Her feedback was instrumental in the production of this*
> *book. I love you, Alora.*

The only downside to the surreal setting was that it was mid-September and the temperatures were dropping below freezing at night. Had it been warmer, we would have stayed longer, but the chilly winds and dark skies were indicative of the changing season – especially at the higher elevations.

"It sure is gloomy today," I moaned, "and they're forecasting rain for later this week."

"That's not good," Sam replied as she handed me a ham and cheese sandwich on a crusty roll that she'd made me for breakfast. "I was so cold last night that I had trouble sleeping. Perhaps we should get off this mountain before we get snowed on."

> *Then tragedy struck...*

As I bit into the sandwich, a dental crown on my front tooth popped off. After a moment of fishing for it with my tongue, I spit it out into my palm.

"Oh my gosh, you're gruesome!" Sam kidded. "You look like a Swiss hillbilly…if that's a thing."

"Yikes!" I said, looking into her pocket mirror. "It's amazing how much a missing tooth can affect your appearance. Well, I guess that settles

☼ 𝍫 ◉

it – let's get off this mountain and get my chopper fixed. Hopefully there's a dentist in Interlaken that can see me."

Shortly after beginning the descent down the crushed granite road, Greeny's freewheel seized. When this malfunction happens, the pedals turn with the wheels – so the bike can no longer coast freely. It's especially dangerous on a tandem bike because the two sets of cranks, linked by a chain, can whip around with great force. If you're out of sync with your partner or suddenly stop pedaling, ligaments can shred and bones can break.

To make matters worse, each pedal has a little metal tooth on the back of it to flip the toe-clips upright to insert your shoe. Although cage-style toe-clips were outdated at the time, we liked them because they allowed us to wear an assortment of footwear while touring.

"Ouch!" Sam squealed. "The bike just bit me. It's like pedaling an eggbeater."

Rather than making the prudent choice of descending slowly, we chose to go as fast as possible – holding our legs away from the gyrating mess. Seeing us racing back into town with our bloody legs held out, flashing a gap-toothed smile, must have been a comical sight.

We stopped at the Fremdemverkhersamt tourist information office for help finding a bike shop and dentist. I went inside while Sam stayed with the bike.

I returned with good news: "There's a bike shop down the street and a dentist a block away. His name is Doctor Finger…I was told it's a common last name around here."

"Doctor Finger? You've got to be kidding me," Sam giggled. "Are you sure he's not a proctologist? What's his first name, Slippy?"

Chapter 47
Europapark

A few overcast days later, we reached Basel – an immaculate park-like city on the Rhine near the German border. Using the GPS to find the river, we straddled it northward as darkness fell.

After an uneventful crossing into Germany, we were greeted by our old friend, the German Radweg. It was smooth as glass, and camping was permitted anywhere along the grassy bank carved from the evergreen forest. On the opposite bank was France.

After a restful night under some tall pines, we were up at dawn and wheeling along. It was surprising how uninhabited this stretch of the river was – reminiscent of the lonely stretch in Austria that nearly brought us to our knees. Late in the afternoon, when the skies became heavy and the winds began to howl, we sought shelter from the oncoming storm.

"This place is so cute, let's see if they have a vacancy," Sam said as we rode up to a Gasthaus that looked like a big cuckoo clock.

"Take a bite out of it and see if it's made of gingerbread," I kidded.

Thankfully, we checked in just before the rain and lightning struck. I went straight to the bar before going to the room – a normal practice of mine, especially in this country.

"Ah, Mutter's Milch," I said, tasting one. "Let's take a bunch of Por qué no's back to the room while we freshen up."

The next day we rode into the storied Black Forest region of Germany. The rolling countryside grew hillier the further northeast we traveled. By the time we reached the resort town of Rust, we were exhausted from all the undulations.

Although Rust looks like every other quaint village in the area, it's the home of Europapark – Europe's largest theme park at the time. The adjacent campground, Camp Ticonderoga, has an endearing western theme – with a saloon, teepee village, and fire pits. We pitched the tent in a field full of campervans and rode into town for dinner.

☼ 🏃 ⊙

"Look, Honey, they've got Käsespätzle!" Sam cheered as she perused the menu.

Keenly aware of the risk and ramifications, we both ordered it. When we returned to the campground, there was a group of rowdy Austrians singing Tyrolean ballads in the gazebo. We decided to join the party.

A buff blond lad there, named Angus, expressed his undying love for American football. He even gets up in the middle of the night to watch the games live and dreams of traveling around America during the NFL playoffs to see them all in person.

The next morning, we stored our valuables in the campground lockers, put our bike in secured storage, and went into the park.

"It sure is less chaotic than Gardaland," I whispered to Sam as we walked calmly in. "I sure don't miss being trampled by Italians in tank tops."

Similar to Epcot's World Showcase, each section of the park is themed after a different country – in this case, all European. We'd heard good things about the park and expected the thrill rides to be state-of-the-art. We weren't disappointed. After a full day of rollercoasters, pirate boat rides, and haunted houses, we made our way back to the tent – only to find that it had been ransacked.

"We've been robbed!" Sam said as she jumped inside to survey the damage. "Good thing we locked everything up – from what I can tell, they only took a tube of sunscreen."

When I reported the incident to the campground manager, he was shocked. Apparently, theft was rare.

"The thieves must have known to hit our tent. It appears no one else was robbed. Whoever did this must have known we were on a long trip and had everything with us," I deduced. "I bet Angus or one of his friends had something to do with it."

☼   🏃   ◉

Chapter 48
The Forest Elf

Germany's Black Forest is indeed on the dark side. The tall pines with draping needles grow so tightly together that the forest floor barely sees the sun. The terrain is challenging too. The relentless grades and chilly northern winds had us stopping often for warm bowls of goulash.

One afternoon, we pulled into a Gasthaus at the bottom of a forested glen. Exhausted from climbing thousands of vertical feet that day, we hoped to find a cozy place to rest and do laundry.

We were greeted at the front door by a no-nonsense-ninety-year-old forest elf with the strength of seven men. Immediately after checking us in, she grabbed our packs and dashed up the stairs to show us to our room on the third floor. She waited for us to catch up before opening the door.

"Wow, I bet she'd be a great stoker," I joked as we chased after her.

She plopped our bags down in the sparsely furnished room and started to scurry away. I stopped her to ask if we could do laundry.

"Ja, naturalich," she replied, stretching out her arms to accept it.

After gathering everything in our packs, we asked her to wait outside so we could strip off the clothes we were wearing. Since we carried so few garments, it was important to do as much laundry as possible. Once disrobed, I slid the remaining articles out the front door. She collected them and pitter-pattered down the stairs. We knew she'd do her best to get them cleaner than they'd ever been before.

Several hours passed, and Sam was getting frustrated. "Ugh, where's that laundry? I'm starving, the kitchen is closing soon, and I've got nothing to wear to dinner."

Since there wasn't a phone in the room, I slinked downstairs to investigate in the only clean clothes I had, a pair of Lycra bike shorts.

⚓ 🧍 ☉

"Ooh!" the little elf hooted when she saw me coming down the stairs half-naked. She scampered away to get her giant son to deal with me.

He broke the bad news: "Everything is being washed right now, and we don't have a dryer. We just hang everything in the furnace room overnight. Don't worry though, it will be totally dry by morning."

Back in the room, I remembered a gift I'd purchased and began rummaging through my panniers to find it. A few minutes later, Sam and I descended the stairs dressed for dinner. I was wearing Tim's birthday present, a cycling jersey with a Swiss cross on it, and Sam had a rain jacket on, and only a rain jacket on, that she wore like a dress. An incredibly short and ridiculous dress.

The bashful little elf reluctantly seated us in the crowded dining room. Although she was keenly aware of our dilemma, it didn't make the situation any less awkward. After seating us, she darted around the establishment, serving the tables and managing the front desk. She had boundless energy, yet no time for small talk. I found that out the hard way when I asked about a word on the dessert menu.

"Entschuldigung, bitte, was ist eine Birne?"

"Eine Birne ist eine Birne," she replied.

"Ja, aber was ist eine Birne?"

Clearly, she was irritated by my ignorance. "Eine Birne ist eine Birne."

I shrugged my shoulders…

"EINE BIRNE IST EINE BIRNE!" She hollered. Then she threw her arms up in exasperation, shuffled off into the kitchen, and returned with something in her hand.

"Birne," she said, holding up a pear.

"Thank goodness," I whispered to Sam, "for a moment there, I thought she was going in the kitchen to grab a meat cleaver."

The next morning, we stuffed our clean laundry into our soiled packs and got on the road early. There are few things more comforting on a bike tour than a pack full of clean clothes.

☀ 🏃 ⊚

As we rode away, we rang the bell and waved goodbye to the little elf on the front porch. She smiled and waved back. Then she grabbed a load of firewood twice her size and bolted back inside.

"Did you notice that the only time she smiled was when we were leaving?"

"No doubt she's happy to see us go," Sam giggled, "but hey, at least we left a lasting impression. She won't forget us anytime soon."

Chapter 49
Birthplace of a River

The crisp autumn mornings and bitterly cold nights had us seeking shelter indoors more than usual. Camping wasn't very fun anymore – and the plummeting temperatures, physical exhaustion, and overexposure had us feeling worn down. Our muscles were depleted and felt achy and sore all the time.

By this time, most of the campgrounds were closed for the season, which meant showers and laundry facilities were harder to come by – and the nippy winds had us regretting coming so far north.

The changing season heightened the journey's sense of finality. With the finish line only a few hundred miles away, we were melancholy about reaching Munich. We knew California would be wonderfully warm that time of year, and we looked forward to seeing friends and family, but part of us wished the adventure could go on forever.

On the outskirts of Münsingen, we climbed a mountain to meet the Danube River at its birthplace. After a grueling ascent, we crested the ridge, and slid off the backside next to a tiny creek that would become the great river.

It's a beautiful region with scenic surprises around every bend. Sheer rock faces, large boulders, and lush green valleys greet you as you snake your way through the pastoral canyon. It was nice to be back on the Donau Radweg too – the same bike path we'd ridden across Austria months before – when the river was still warm enough to swim in.

The following day we entered Bavaria and raced for Munich across the rolling agricultural plains of southern Germany. Having lived there as a college intern for an automotive company, it felt like a homecoming. I have such fond memories of that epic summer in Munich:

> *On my first day of work, the stern lady in H.R., for whom I'd brought a bouquet of flowers, had some troubling news:*

☼   ⚗   ◉

"The factory will be closed all August for retooling – so there won't be any work then."

"No work for an entire month? I wasn't aware of that. I really need to earn money for college – so that's a problem."

"No, it isn't," she said matter-of-factly, "it's a paid vacation."

The thought of a month of paid vacation after only two months of work, not to mention a free apartment, was mind-boggling to me. I bought an unlimited Eurail pass and backpacked all around Europe with some college buddies – using my apartment as a home base.

After a late night on the town, we'd hop on an overnight train going anywhere and sleep wherever we could. You can cover a lot of ground if you don't mind waking up groggy from "train wine" in a new country each day. I'll never forget the morning I woke up in the aisle of a crowded Portuguese train with shoeprints all over my T-shirt.

The most memorable moment, however, came within four hours of being in England for the first time. After checking into a hostel, I went for a run while my friends took a nap. I dashed out the front door, rounded a high hedge, and nearly bowled over Lady Di and Prince Harry. Unbeknownst to me, it was Harry's first day of school at an academy next door.

"Oh my!" she gasped, pulling her son to her side.

I immediately recognized her; she was one of the most famous people in the world at the time. Then I noticed a police barricade across the street with paparazzi behind it – perhaps the same people that caused her death in a Paris tunnel eight years later. It dawned on me that I could have been perceived as a threat and even shot. When I got back from my run, I was excited to tell my buddies about how accessible the Royals are in such a small country.

Another perk of my engineering internship was that production workers in Bavaria were allowed to drink beer on the job – since it's considered food. The snack bars inside the factory sold a variety of fine lagers – and there were designated bottle holders on the assembly line for each worker. Some of the other interns abused the privilege, though. In mid-July, a disturbing sign was posted above the beer section that read:

Irländer Verboten

They deserved it. The wild Irish lads that lived in my building were drunk all day and raising hell all night. Their apartment was full of street signs and construction barriers collected from all over Munich.

One night they even convinced me to jump a twelve-foot fence in Olympic Park to get into a disco for free – but we ended up jumping the wrong fence and landing smack-dab in the middle of the Davis Cup award ceremonies by mistake. The security guards grabbed us by the arms, walked us past the gawking crowd of tennis elite, and literally threw us out the gate.

That crazy summer whetted my wanderlust for aimless adventure travel – a chronic condition that inspired the journey I was currently on.

Sam and I spent our final night of stealth-camping in a damp Bavarian forest, eating soggy sandwiches in our sleeping bags – because it was too cold to be out of them.

We pushed hard for Munich the next day, reaching Dachau just before nightfall. Prior to checking into a hotel, we took a sobering lap around the courtyard of the former concentration camp there – the very

✡ 🕎 ☉

first one. It was hard to imagine that just sixty years prior, the free and open Europe we'd just ridden around was being ravaged by war. There's a monument there with an inscription that reads:

"Never Again."

☼ 🕯 ◉

Chapter 50
The Victory Party

Our plan was to put the bike in storage at the Munich Airport and hop on a train to Oktoberfest. As we rode along the Radweg next to the Isar River, we could see planes taking off and landing in the distance. With the final destination in sight, we fantasized about doing nothing.

"When we get home, I'm going to sit on the couch and watch TV for the foreseeable future."

"That sounds great!" Sam hooted. "I'm going to crank up the heat, crack a bottle of wine, and take a bubble bath until my hands get all pruney – like I did at the winery in Austria."

We stopped at a shipping depot near the airport to retrieve the package I mailed myself from Vienna.

"Hey, look, here it is," I said, proudly holding up a spare tandem axle that I found in the parcel. "I knew I'd brought one."

"Yeah, but you don't get credit for it because you didn't have it when we needed it. Sorry, Buster, no credit for you."

At the airport, we dismounted Greeny for the last time, put her in storage, and hopped a train full of locals in lederhosen to the campground nearest Oktoberfest.

We went for the party – and left with P.T.S.D.

The conditions at Thalkirchen campground were appalling. Like Fusina, there were party-tour pup tents pitched as far as the eye could see – with so many empty beer bottles littering the grass that it was hazardous to walk around.

We were too tired to look for another campground, and all the nearby hotels were already booked, so we cleared a spot and settled in for some much-needed rest. We were already in our sleeping bags as our neighbors headed out for the evening.

☼ 🏃 ◉

"Looks like a good night to put in earplugs," Sam moaned. "They're already drunk and singing."

"That's for sure. Based on past experience, you need 30 decibel ones to drown-out a drunk Australian."

Wave after wave of boisterous boozers marched past our tent throughout the night. We barely slept a wink.

After some sightseeing the next morning, we arrived at Oktoberfest ready to rock. The scale of the event is something to behold. There were twenty big-top tents, each packed with three thousand people, with an oom-pah band in the middle playing to a sing-along crowd.

There are endless racks of rotisseries roasting a variety of meats over an open spit, and automated conveyor belts washing and refilling liter Bier Steins. By the end of the evening, everyone is standing on the benches, swaying arm-in-arm, and having a rip-roaring good time.

"It's funny, if they served hopped-up beer in gigantic glass mugs at festivals in America, there'd be issues."

Sam laughed, "No doubt about that. Watered-down beer in plastic cups gets punchy enough."

We clinked mugs and toasted, "Cheers, Rabbit Ears."

"Cheers, Danny-bear. Here's to the ultimate year off; I can't think of any better victory party than this."

We awoke to whipping winds and stormy skies the next morning. When nature called, I reluctantly crawled out of my cocoon to run to the bathroom.

What happened next will forever haunt me...

The walls of the men's restroom were smeared with human excrement, and the floor was awash in bodily fluids. While squatting over the least disgusting toilet, I tragically lost my balance and bumped my bare butt against a poo-covered partition. When I reached for toilet paper to wipe it off, I felt wetness – someone had urinated on every roll in the bathroom. Dashing for the shower with my pants around my ankles, I slipped in a puddle of vomit and landed in it. As I rolled around, trying to

☼　🕉　◉

stand up, I slipped in it again. When I finally reached the shower, I ripped off my clothes and turned the knob.

Nothing happened.

It required a token – which could be conveniently purchased at the campground store. So I waddled my unwiped ass back to the tent to get the money to buy one.

"I'm so frickin' ready to go home," I said, poking my head inside the tent. "Without going into details, I'm covered in vomit and poop and generally having a bad day."

Just then, it started to rain.

Sensing my fragile state, Sam ran to the store to get tokens and toilet paper. We cleaned up, packed up, and checked into an airport hotel to catch our flight home the next day.

The hotel felt luxurious – like the one in Phoenix did after so many months of sailing. As we looked out the rain-pelted window, we felt blessed to be warm and dry. If you live outside long enough, you'll never take shelter for granted again.

"So tell me," Sam asked, "of all the places we were in Europe, where was your favorite?"

"Right now, I'd have to say…inside."

☼   ⚚   ⊛

Chapter 51
The Verdict

We ended up cycling three thousand miles around nine countries – roughly the same distance that we sailed. Our strategy of riding alongside rivers paid off well; we rolled alongside the Adige, Arve, Borne, Danube, Inn, Isar, Neckar, Tovara, Rhine, and Rhône – stopping for an occasional swim. We cycled as far north as Amsterdam, east as Bratislava, and south as Siena – deep in the hills of Tuscany. And Oktoberfest was one hell of a finale.

Shortly after our plane touched down in sunny California, reality set in. Rather than riding across sunny fields on a warm summer day, I was preparing for the unpleasantness of defending myself in court.

Although it was a small case, I took it personally. I spent the next couple of weeks gathering evidence and testimonials to support my narrative. Without any arrests or convictions, nothing could be proven, but I hoped the judge would find my deductions from the security deposit reasonable based on the misuse alleged by local law enforcement.

Violet and her scowling mother slipped into the courtroom just as the proceedings were scheduled to begin. She avoided all eye contact.

When it was my turn to speak, I stated that I'd been contacted by the Sheriff's Office informing me that my house had been turned into a suspected brothel. I expressed my opinion about who may have been the mastermind and operative of the alleged one-whore hideaway. My plea was passionate, persuasive, and colorful. Let's just say Grouchy would have been proud. The judge seemed amused by my antics, but stopped me before I finished to inform me that rental laws pertaining to deposits are pretty cut-and-dry in the State of California – and that any alleged breaches to a lease agreement would need to be remedied in a different case.

When it was Violet's turn to speak, she distanced herself from the situation, saying that she may have sublet part of the house to someone who might have been giving sensual massages without her knowledge.

"Sensual massages?" the judge chuckled.

My closing argument appealed to the judge's sensibility using Violet's own words. I argued that if she sublet the property, then she violated the lease agreement – and if the sublessee used it as a sensual massage parlor, then there were extenuating damages to my property, neighborhood, and reputation. I asked him whether he'd replace locks, linens, and mattresses if it allegedly happened in his house instead of mine.

The judge sifted through the evidence and receipts I provided and said, "As entertaining as this has been, the courts are busy, and I've got everything I need. A decision will be mailed to you in one to two weeks."

We felt pretty good about the proceedings. Regardless of the outcome, we were ready to move on.

A few days later, the verdict arrived in the mail.

"Well, what does it say? Did you win, did you win?" Sam asked excitedly.

"Hold on a second. Geez!" I said, as I struggled to separate the perforated pages. "Crap, I lost and have to return the entire deposit."

Chapter 52
Settling Up in Sedona

O ne month later, on an off-road expedition from California to Maine, Sam and I spoke incessantly about how transformational our sailing and cycling adventure had been…despite the setbacks. Prior to leaving, I returned Luther's guitar and amp to a dank nightclub in the City where he worked. It provided insight into his paltry, putrid life. Fortunately, he wasn't there – I hoped to never see him again.

We drove south to duck the autumn storms, camping in Death Valley and cavorting in Las Vegas, before popping down to Mexico to do some maintenance on Marylee.

When we reached our dusty little sloop in the Sonoran Desert, it wasn't the same. We didn't see any familiar faces in the cantinas – and we felt detached from the cruising community without a boat in the water.

A few days later, we set off for Indiana to spend Thanksgiving with Sam's grandparents. Along the way, we stopped in Sedona to hike among the red rocks.

Sedona is a spiritual place. The native Yavapai-Apache tribes that inhabit the cathedral canyons believe there are four vortexes connecting heaven and earth there. Although I don't believe in vortexes, that didn't stop me from writing out a check to Violet, putting it in an envelope, carrying it to the top of one overlooking Boynton Canyon, and holding it high above my head.

"This settles it. Once it's mailed, it will all be over. The end to a crazy story with a messed up moral about not trusting anyone."

"Yeah, it's kinda messed up, but hey, that's what happened. You followed your heart and got stabbed in the back. All's well that ends well, I guess. I'm just glad it's over. Say, if a story has a moral, isn't it a fable?"

"I'm not so sure," I chuckled, "don't fables have animals in them?"

"Well, there were snakes, sharks, bees, dolphins, squid, and whales, weren't there?"

"Yeah... I guess so. You know, all the crazy stuff that happened might make for an interesting book. What do you think?"

"Absolutely, Honey, you've got to write it down. Just please, please, PLEASE promise you won't write about that Käsespätzle incident in Austria. That'd be really embarrassing. It was an awful scent," she giggled. "I still can't believe that lady said that."

"Don't worry, Sammi; I promise I won't."

After spending a white Christmas with my family in the backwoods of Maine, we returned to Bello Beach in early January. As I was unloading my truck, I bumped into a neighbor who was anxious to tell me about a movie that had been filmed just below my property while I was away.

"It was a major motion picture. They turned Little Beach into a Japanese fishing village. The opening scenes were filmed under the big cypress tree, and the ending was filmed at the overlook."

"Too bad we missed it, what movie were they filming?"

"Memoirs of a Geisha," Matt replied. "How's that for irony?"

Epilogue:
Sailing Into Lightning

Four Months Later…

Home life paled in comparison to our vibrant voyage – like being trapped in a black-and-white movie where the backdrop never changed. I spent my days writing and daydreaming about being back aboard Marylee – strumming Cassidy in some forgotten cove. Sadly, no matter how much porn I watched, I didn't see my house in any films.

It didn't take long for Sam to find a job while I negotiated an offer letter with a start-up. It was spring though, the most beautiful season in the Sea of Cortez; so I fixed to finagle one last month in paradise.

"I'll accept the offer, but I can't start until June," I informed my new employer.

It was that easy. With income in my foreseeable future, I grabbed my flippers, adjusted my attitude, and hit the road. Unfortunately, Sam was committed and couldn't come – so I invited some friends to join me.

"Hey Dad, I'm heading to Mex to do some cruising. Want to come?"

"You bet," Dick replied without hesitation. "I'll be ready to go by the time you get here."

Although he didn't have much experience on the water, as a retired Air Force aviator, I knew he'd appreciate the similarities between sailing and soaring. When I arrived, he was waiting for me outside, next to his well-worn green canvas duffle bag. We kissed my mother goodbye, thanked her for the cookies she'd baked, and drove until late in the night.

As we were bombing down Mexico's Federal Highway 15 the following day, after crossing the border in Nogales, we passed a man stretched-out in the bed of his pick-up on the shoulder of the busy roadway. He had a cowboy hat pulled down over his eyes.

"Boy, this sure is a casual country," Dick laughed. "You've got to love that about Mexico."

☼ ⸸ ☉

Moments later, we were pulled over by a Federale brandishing a speed gun. When he threatened to confiscate my driver's license and take me to jail in Hermosillo for excessive speed, I tossed sixty bucks on the seat of his cruiser.

He nodded, commented on the beautiful weather, and wished me a "buen viaje."

It took three long days to prepare Marylee for the overnight passage to Baja. With the tanks filled and an icebox bulging with beer, we pushed away one perfect afternoon and hoisted the sails at sundown.

We knifed through the buttery waters under a chandeliered starry sky. When I ducked below to refill my coffee tumbler, I caught a glimpse of my father at the helm. I'll never forget that grin – in command, once again, of a ship upon the wind.

As dawn broke, the warm hues of Baja were revealed on the horizon. After rounding Punta Domingo, we sailed wing-on-wing into the protected waters of Conception Bay. We anchored off Playa Santa Barbara and collapsed in our bunks from the overnight effort. A few hours later, I awoke to find my dad in the cockpit, under the umbrella, sipping his signature vodka tonic.

"Get your candy-ass out of bed and mix yourself a cocktail," he hollered. "You almost slept through happy hour."

I rubbed the sleep from my eyes, poured one, and joined him outside. There's a certain "je ne sais quoi" of tranquility in Baja that's impossible to describe.

Although we did the same activities every day, each felt unique. We'd fish in the morning, read in the afternoon, play bocce ball at dusk, and return to Marylee to grill the catch of the day each evening. As we dined outside by candlelight, my dad opened up about his challenging childhood and military career more than ever before.

At the age of four, he spent six months in an iron lung – a nasty contraption where only your head protrudes. The hospital nurses placed him near a window so he could look down on the other children playing in the playground below.

✵ ☥ ◉

Then, at the age of six, he was tragically orphaned when both of his parents died within six months of each other. He and his three siblings were separated to live with various family members; he was sent to one that needed an extra hand on the farm. Although he always felt loved, losing his family and home at such an impressionable age was probably the reason he stuttered as a child – and undoubtedly the reason he cherished having a family so much now.

Determined to improve his life, he got a night-job shucking oysters on a wharf in Boston Harbor to put himself through college. Too poor to afford a coat, apparently his sister, Florence, brought him one while he was working outside one bitterly cold winter night.

Everything improved after college. He joined the Air Force, graduated at the top of his class from flight school – and ultimately became a Lt. Colonel. His reward for receiving top honors was a choice of where to be stationed. He chose England.

There, he enjoyed a golden age of aviation – when pilots had liberties they'd never have again. He and some buddies even bought a vintage biplane to fly around in. Since they didn't have a car, they'd hand-crank the prop and fly around the countryside looking for a pub with a nearby grassy field to land in.

When they weren't flying missions, they'd try crossing the Irish Channel in their underpowered aircraft, but were forced to turn around on several occasions when unfavorable headwinds caused them to run low on fuel.

One of my favorite stories is when he landed in Liberia just after it was liberated. He was one of the first Americans to arrive there. As soon as his plane came to a stop, the locals rushed him and surrounded his plane, holding up buckets. They'd heard America was bringing them freedom – and they brought buckets to carry it back in.

He spoke about his wartime missions in Vietnam, when his C-7 Caribou was shot up as he attempted corkscrew landings into special forces' outposts behind enemy lines. Apparently, his squadron took heavy losses.

⚓ 🕴 ⊙

Although he'd never accept being called a hero, the
Presidential medals I pinned to his uniform, as I was
dressing him to be buried, said otherwise.

A product of the greatest generation, he was proud, but
never prideful.

The next day, I took him snorkeling for the first time. Having lived in great diving spots throughout his life, including a two-year stint in the Philippines, he regretted not trying it sooner.

As we moved from cove to cove, we eventually caught up with Geary in his thatched hut on Burro Beach, wearing his signature dark sunglasses with a rolled-up red bandana around his head. Although my father was a disciplined "by-the-book" kind of guy when I was growing up, the older he got, the less rigid he became – adopting a "whatever-floats-your-boat" attitude. He respected Geary for carving out a simple lifestyle that made him happy.

"It's a quiet place where not much happens. Hope it stays that way," Geary chortled.

From my experience, Geary's place was anything but quiet. He's such a welcoming person, and so helpful to cruisers that he has legions of friends that visit him regularly. In fact, while we were chatting, three sailboats arrived and dinghied in to see him. Dick was delighted to learn that all three captains were retired Navy F-18 pilots who had been cruising together for several years.

Someone suggested that we have a clambake on the beach that evening, so we all spent the rest of the day digging for chocolatas and butter clams on a nearby sandbar. After a potluck dinner, we each picked a musical instrument from Geary's music basket and played and sang around the crackling bonfire until late in the night.

A couple days later, anchored off Santispac, we were running low on provisions and needed to hitchhike into Mulegé. As soon as I stuck out my thumb, a Mexican family stopped, and we jumped in the back of their pickup. It was a revelation for my father to live so carefree. He even took a bucket shower at Bertha's, which he proclaimed to be "the most interesting shower" he'd ever taken.

While we were in town, he bought a bus ticket to San Diego for later that week. When the time came for him to leave, we hitchhiked back into Mulegé and were having cocktails at a nearby cantina.

"Thanks for coming down, Dad; you're a great first mate."

"And you're a fine captain, Daniel. I can see why you love cruising so much. It's an amazing lifestyle. When you invited me down, I just asked myself, "¿Por qué no?"

When the bus arrived, he tossed his bag in the luggage compartment, climbed the stairs, and disappeared behind the tinted windows. Although I was sad to see him go, I was happy to have spent more quality time with him than ever before.

> *In his twilight years, he considered our adventure to be one of the best times of his life. I'd been reading from this book to him the night he died, nine years later. In the final hours, as he slowly slipped away, he started hallucinating about being back aboard Marylee. He reminded me to tie up the dinghy just before dying in my arms.*

Alone again, I hitchhiked back to Marylee to tackle some messy boat projects I'd been postponing until I had more space. Other than some long-billed birds poking holes in the inflatable dinghy, trying to open up clams, there was no negativity.

Tim arrived a few days later. As expected, we went hard by day and even harder by night – closing cantinas and munching on midnight street tacos.

> *It reminded me of the time he and I mountain biked around Ireland in our mid-twenties. It was a country-wide pub crawl. We ruffled many feathers along the way – just getting back from a long night out after the B&B innkeepers had already served breakfast.*

☼ 🏃 ☉

*I barfed a lot on that trip, even while I was riding, and was
mystified by how unfazed the Irish girls were by it. They'd
hold my bucket, wipe my mouth, and kiss me without any
hesitation.*

One day, while trolling off Punta Domingo, Tim caught a strange
looking fish. He held it up and looked it directly in the eyes.

"What should we do with this thing? I doubt anything this ugly
would taste very good."

"Heck if I know," I replied, "but if we're not going to eat it, we
should throw it back."

We found out later that it was a Cornetfish – a delicacy and a
missed opportunity.

The day before his departure, Tim's sunglasses blew off the dinghy
as we were spearfishing around a rock in the middle of the bay. We tried to
find them in forty feet of water but couldn't in the muted afternoon
sunlight.

Just after Tim left to catch a plane out of Los Cabos, a red sloop
pulled in and anchored next to me. It was being singlehanded by a young
captain named Dovie – a cool cat I had a lot in common with. Since it's
always safer to dive with a buddy, I invited him to go spearfishing with me
the following day in the same spot Tim lost his sunglasses.

Immediately after jumping in the water, I spotted them flashing on
the bottom and recovered them. Then Dovie and I swam into deeper water
at the base of the giant rock. He spotted something, dove down, and
speared a large amberjack through its midsection.

Rather than swimming away, this thirty-pound fish turned and
attacked him. Dovie managed to unsheathe the knife strapped to his ankle
and stab the demon in the skull before it bit him. Had he hesitated, there
would have been blood in the water. Although I always carried a knife
while spearfishing to cut away a powerful fish if it ever started pulling me
down, I never envisioned using it to defend myself from dinner.

☼ 🏃 ◉

A few days later, my final guest arrived to help me sail Marylee back to San Carlos. He'd flown into Los Cabos and hopped on a bus to Santispac. Having no idea when he would actually arrive, I watched for his bus to rumble around the mountain curve until late in the night. When it finally did, I jumped in the dinghy and met him on the beach.

"Mr. Slasher, I presume," I huffed aristocratically.

"Good to see you, Danger. Oh man, it took all day to get here. I'm ready for some Por qué no's."

Once aboard Marylee, he took a shot of Tequila, dove off the bow, climbed up the swim ladder, took another shot, and dove back in again.

We spent the remaining days exploring my favorite anchorages. One evening we played bocce ball with the founder of a famous commune in Tennessee known as "The Farm." He contended that communes are wonderful when they begin, with likeminded people that all work together, but collapse under the weight of newcomers that won't pull their own. In his opinion, cruising is the perfect communal lifestyle because every captain is forced to be self-reliant, yet is coddled in camaraderie and common purpose.

Although the weather was pleasant, the air grew stickier with each passing day. The increased moisture spawned widespread thunderstorms throughout the region. Although lightning is a common occurrence on the mainland during the summer, where the moist marine air collides with the cool, dry air as it rises up the mountain slopes, there aren't as many electrical storms on the Baja side – especially in the springtime. We huddled around the single sideband receiver to hear Don on Summer Passage deliver his weather forecast on the Amigo-net each evening.

"Expect continued thunderstorms up and down the Sea. There's a tropical flow firmly in place that's going to keep it unsettled for the foreseeable future."

"Well, Don, that's an unsettling forecast," Slasher groaned. "Dude, I've got to get back to my job. Do you think we'll be able to cross in time for me to catch my flight out of Phoenix?"

"Good question. The summer weather seems to have set in early this year and could stay unsettled until fall. I've got to get back too; I'm supposed to start a new job in a week. I need to get Marylee back to San Carlos, though; it's the only marina with dry storage around here – and besides, that's where my car is parked."

"Well, I guess we'll be sailing into lightning then."

"Not necessarily. You could catch a bus to San Diego or a flight out of La Paz or Los Cabos, and I could singlehand her back."

"Forget that. Buying a bus ticket and a last-minute flight, after eating a nonrefundable ticket home from Phoenix doesn't sound very appealing to me. Plus, that would mean you'd have to sail Marylee across the Sea and decommission her yourself. Let's just stick to the original plan… if you think we can cross safely."

"Well, the seas are flat and the wind is moderate. Other than some isolated cells, the weather seems pretty benign. Even if there are thunderstorms, we should be able to see them on the radar and steer around them. If we had more time, we could wait for the skies to clear, but since we don't, maybe we should just go for it."

"I'm good with that, but I sure don't want to get struck at sea in this confined space."

While it's true that a metal mast on the open ocean is susceptible to being struck, I'd had good success dodging thunderstorms thus far. When sailing in the tropics, sometimes the only option you have is to proceed with caution. If you're out on the big blue long enough, eventually you'll be caught in an electrical storm.

Thankfully, we were in saltwater. Lightning is even more dangerous in freshwater because it lacks the salinity to transfer energy away. In fact, 90% of pleasure craft struck in freshwater sink, whereas only 10% suffer the same fate in saltwater. Still, the damage to life and property can be catastrophic – even if the boat appears relatively unscathed.

As a precautionary measure, I devised a cabling system to carry the energy away from Marylee's interior. Although boats can't be grounded unless they're touching the seafloor, by attaching cables to the metal standing rigging and hanging them over the side of the boat, it creates a path of least resistance to the water and shields the interior like a

Faraday cage. The intent is to direct energy around the boat instead of blowing a hole through it.

Slasher scoffed, "Do you really expect that contraption to dissipate three million volts? It won't matter anyway; we'll already be fried from the transient energy."

Although my invention was probably just wishful thinking, at least it felt proactive. We sat in the cockpit and watched the weather. As the sun began to set, the skies began to clear.

"That's more blue sky than we've had all week," I said, looking through the binoculars. "It's now or never, Mr. Slasher; please prepare the ship for departure."

"Aye, aye, Captain! Bottoms up and anchors away!"

He chugged the remainder of his Por qué no and headed to the foredeck to weigh anchor. After rounding the reef at the entrance to the bay, where a flashing white light on a rusty red pole marks the hazard, we set a course for San Carlos. A few minutes later, we saw a foreboding sight – a dozen fishing boats steaming into port.

"That's unnerving; it looks like they're all headed for Santa Rosalia. I wonder if they know something we don't."

Slasher wasn't spooked. "You can't read too much into it. It could just be local boats returning from a day of fishing."

"You're right, there's no reason to jump to conclusions… but it does seem kind of strange."

The winds were blowing favorably from the west – pushing us squarely from behind. The seas were flat, the stars were out, and the Por qué no's were in abundant supply. We were having a marvelous time…until Slasher saw a strike in the distance.

"Did you see that? Lightning to the north – at nine o'clock."

We stared in that direction for several minutes but saw nothing but billowy white clouds against a purple horizon.

I disregarded it, saying, "It must have been a stray discharge, perhaps from a long distance away. There doesn't seem to be any activity now. Besides, even if there's lightning to the north, it shouldn't affect us if the wind keeps blowing from the west."

☼ ⚓ ☉

After a quiet hour, we deemed it a fluke and confidently steamed ahead.

Suddenly, there was another flash…

Slasher peered through the binoculars and said, "Looks like there's a front moving in from the north."

"That's concerning. The good news is we're already halfway there – only forty-six miles to go. If all goes well, we'll be anchored in a few more hours."

Unfortunately, it wasn't going to be that easy…

The frequency of strikes intensified the further east we went. Thankfully, we still had stars above our mast, at least for now, but the clouds were moving in quickly.

A few hours later, with only twenty-five miles to go, there was a strike directly in front of us.

"Crap, now it's between us and San Carlos!" I shouted. "Let's head south, toward Guaymas, and try to duck it."

After a few uneventful minutes of traveling in that direction, there was another blinding strike directly in front of us – this time even closer than the previous one. There was no delay between the flash of light and the sound of clapping thunder.

Slasher had more bad news: "Now there's a front moving in from the south. It looks like we're caught in the crosshairs between the cool, moist air coming up from the tropics and the hot, dry air coming down from Arizona."

The wind suddenly reversed direction and began blasting us with gale-force easterlies. Waves began buffeting Marylee's bow, slowing forward progress and kicking up a stinging spray.

By the time we reefed the mainsail, there were several strikes per minute. The shrieking wind and whipped-up seas heightened the sense of

�֍ ⚡ ⊙

calamity. As conditions deteriorated, there was so much surface scatter on the radar that it was difficult to distinguish the thunderheads.

"Slash, please go below and gather all the electronics we aren't using and put them in the oven. Hopefully, the metal housing will shield them from EMF. And get the life raft and ditch bag ready in case we go down quickly."

Slasher untethered his harness and went below while I steered. He emerged a few minutes later, just in time to witness a natural phenomenon. After a flurry of strikes, a brilliant ball of electricity shot from the sky and appeared to skip across the surface of the water.

"Ball lightning!" he yelled over the madness. "It's incredibly rare – like a cosmic Roman candle."

It was a bad omen. I went below, pulled the satellite telephone out of the oven, and phoned Sam at three o'clock in the morning. The phone rang several times before she picked it up.

"Hello," she answered in a raspy voice.

"Sorry to call so late, Honey, but we're caught in an electrical storm – and it doesn't look good. Please write down our position in case you need to relay it to the Coast Guard. I'm so glad you're safe at home and not out here with us right now."

"You guys will be alright. I know you will. Keep me updated – and know that I love you."

I hung up the phone feeling bad for upsetting her – and even worse for putting my boat and crew in harm's way once again with no apparent escape.

"Screw this!" I said, gunning Yanmar for San Carlos. "There's a harbor surrounded by high peaks just twenty miles in front of us. If we can just punch through the squalls, we'll be out of this mess in a couple of hours."

"I totally disagree. If we go in this direction, we'll be struck for sure. Going back to Baja is our only safe option."

"Perhaps, but it seems pointless to try to outrun the weather. It's over seventy miles back to Baja, and this boat only averages six knots. I'd rather be struck near land than in the middle of the Sea."

☼ ☥ ☉

Yeah, but if we can just keep that star above our mast," he said, pointing to it, "we might have a chance."

Trusting Slasher's judgment more than my own, I called, "Jibe ho, coming about," and turned Marylee around.

It was immediately more comfortable being blown back to Baja. Still terrifying but much less bumpy, the lightning was in hot pursuit.

"We need to go faster; it's gaining on us."

"Sorry Slash, she won't go much faster, but if we can reach Isla San Marcos before we get caught, we can hide under the high bluffs there. The land will get struck before we will."

"Oh man, that's still several hours away; it's going to be close."

We trimmed the sails with each puff of wind, trying to maximize our speed as if we were racing in a regatta. Thankfully, a favorable current pushed us northward – the direction we needed to go. With only twenty miles left to safety and Slasher's lucky star still above the mast, there was hope.

Suddenly there was a tremendous strike directly in front of us.

"You've got to be kidding me!" I screamed as if we had been unfairly condemned. "Now there's lightning coming in from the Baja side, too. We've been within twenty miles of either side, but now there's nowhere left to run. It's checkmate."

Out of options, we held our course for Isla San Marcos and sailed directly into the lightning. The radar told a chilling tale – we were completely surrounded by thunderheads. As Slasher's lucky star became obscured by one of them, we braced for a strike.

There was a blinding flash and a cracking clap just off Marylee's bow. For a moment, I was certain she'd been struck. Relieved that she hadn't been, we knew the next one would hit us. We crouched down low in the cockpit and covered our heads.

"Thanks for the valiant effort, Slash. I'm afraid it's not going to be a matter of if we get struck; it's going to be a matter of how many times."

☼   🎿   ◉

"Stay away from the lifelines and anything else metal. Everything's going to become energized. Whatever happens, it was nice sailing with you, Danger – even though you did try to kill me every time we went out."

Then something remarkable happened...

As dawn broke, the tops of the clouds lit up. Moments later, we felt the sun's warming glow on our cheeks. At that very moment, the thunderhead moved directly over us. After running all night, we'd finally been caught. But the strike never came. In fact, the lightning stopped altogether, and the clouds began to dissipate. Apparently the sunshine on the cloud formations had saved us.

We began jumping for joy as the skies began to clear – somehow we'd dodged another bullet. The chartplotter recorded the entire ordeal – the panicked circles we made before hightailing it back to Baja.

Threat averted, we headed to a more protected anchorage off Punta Chivato to get some rest. We cracked Por qué no's and toasted life. Once the anchor was set, I called Sam with the good news.

"I knew you guys would be alright. You sailors are always telling fish stories."

Since conditions had improved and the forecast looked good, we rested and prepared for another attempt that evening. For a split-second after I woke up, I wondered if it had just been a bad dream.

"Alright, Mr. Slasher, hopefully you won't wuss out and make me turn around this time," I kidded as we charged back out to sea.

After an easy overnight passage under starry skies, we slipped into the red rock harbor at daybreak. Everyone in San Carlos was talking about the lightning storm the night before – apparently it was one of the worst the locals had ever seen.

"I was up all night watching it from my bedroom window," one lady told us, "praying there weren't any boats out there."

    ☼ ✉ ◉

I thanked Marylee for another fine cruise before putting her in dry storage and racing for the border. Thankfully, we reached Sky Harbor Airport in Phoenix just in time for Slasher to catch his flight home.

Driving alone across the barren desert, I had time to reflect on the trip – and the transformational effect it had on me. After sipping the sweet nectar of freedom, I would never be the same. Now possessions felt like anchors – and I pitied people who lived for place and power, for they would never be content. More healthy, humble, and self-reliant than ever before – the hardships had made me a better person.

I thought about Sam and how brave she was in the scariest of times, and I remembered the laughter we shared in times of joy. I couldn't have done it without her.

I thought about Slasher and how grateful I was to have him there in those moments of despair. I don't know what I would have done without him – all alone on an electric sea.

I thought about Luther, and chuckled about the bindle of brown powder, a driver's license, and a plastic straw I found under a mattress when I was replacing it. Oh, how he must have gone crazy trying to remember where he'd stashed it.

I thought about Gamora and the odd scratches on her face. Perhaps she needed help. Perhaps her parents received an anonymous phone call urging them to come help their daughter.

I thought about Violet. After everything that had allegedly happened, I harbored no animosity toward her. I let it go in Sedona. Now it all just seemed kind of funny.

Hey, some people get termites...

⚓ ⚜ ☉

I was disheartened to learn that she was sentenced to prison for masterminding something completely unrelated a few years later. I had an inexplicable fondness for her, empathy for her upbringing, and hope for her future.

I thought about all the people we met, the magical moments we shared, and the crazy stuff that happened. I eventually concluded that God needs a clown to write it all down – and oh, what a clown I can be.

I then set forth to write the best boat-bike-brothel book ever written – the only published work in the U.S. Library of Congress with a fire pole on its spine. Perhaps my story will inspire other young adventurers to stop and smell the roses while they are most fragrant – and to work hard for their freedom because their lives literally depend on it.

Well, there you have it, a cruiser legend with a messed-up moral:

Follow your heart, but watch your back!

Hey, at least this tawdry tale of treachery has a happy ending. After yarning on so much about sensual massages, I figured you'd probably appreciate one. Go small and go now – and may fair winds and following seas take you safely home.

The End

About the Author:

Sailing Marylee off Mazatlan in 2004

Danny Fitz is an American writer and motivational speaker who lives in Northern California with his wife, Darcy, and son, Luke. He and Sam remain friends to this day.

Through edge-of-your-seat narration, occasionally witty humor, and a tenacity for extreme travel, Danny's goal is to inspire readers to do something remarkable with their lives – no matter what perils may befall them.

His follow-up book, The Corporate Pirate, chronicles a sailing trip down the East Coast and an RV trip back to California while holding a corporate job. Once again, Danny is caught up in a real estate debacle when he finds out the house he's in contract to buy was the scene of Arizona's worst health violation. Wait, what? Rat and tarantula hoarding?

Made in the USA
Las Vegas, NV
02 February 2023

66672645R00142